Essentials of Human Embryology

Essentials of
Human Embryology

Frank D. Allan, M.S., Ph.D.

Associate Professor of Anatomy

The George Washington University School of Medicine, Washington, D. C.

New York · Oxford University Press · 1960

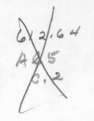
© 1960 by Oxford University Press, Inc.
Library of Congress Catalogue Card Number 60-5097

Printed in the United States of America

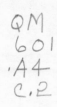
To belabored students and their
time-pressed instructors

It has become apparent that a need exists for a textbook of human embryology of a synoptic nature. With expansion of the medical curriculum has come the inevitable reduction in time available for the study of this subject. Both teacher and student are faced with the problem of condensing the mass of factual material available into a form suitable for consideration in a limited period of time. It is with this in mind that this book has been written. This synopsis will consider the important aspects of human prenatal development and certain features of the adult reproductive systems necessary to explain the establishment, development, and maintenance of the conceptus. It should be realized that in a book of this nature many generalizations have been made and discussions of most controversial issues have been avoided. Thus, many time- and space-consuming discussions are left for the classroom or for additional reading elsewhere.

The material is presented in a manner which is meant to be supplemented by both gross and microscopic anatomy courses. In this respect, only the most basic consideration of the histogenetic aspect of development is presented here, and it is expected that additional information on this subject will be presented as a part of microscopic anatomy. Similarly, only the basic pattern of organ development, etc., has been presented with the thought that many of the changes occurring with growth and maturation will be presented in gross anatomy.

Unlike many textbooks of embryology the consideration of abnormal development has been placed at the end of the book. It is felt that the student can best study teratology after he is familiar with the pattern of normal development. That is not to say, however, that reference to developmental abberations to illustrate a point has no value. (Indeed, the reader is referred to the final chapter at points throughout the work whenever the author feels it lends support to a concept.) However, the consideration of abnormal development *per se* is left until last.

The chapters are arranged and have been written in outline form. As in lectures, a particularly important point may be repeated in order to establish it firmly in the students' minds. This is especially true of the first few chapters where the early stages of development are emphasized. Thus, the study of organs and organ systems is facilitated by the emphasis of the fundamental relationships of early embryonic morphology.

The illustrations included herein have had a heterogenous origin and represent, in most part, a composite of the classical methods of presentation modified by the author's visualization of the processes of development. The latter is, obviously, the product of his training and observation. This has included study of a collection of human embryonic material acquired from various sources.

It is difficult, if not impossible, rightfully to acknowledge all those who have contributed to the field of knowledge this book attempts to tap. It is hoped that an acknowledgement given to the authors of the works cited in the list of references at the end of the book will suffice and allow this book to retain its synoptic nature.

In addition, however, the author would like to express his gratitude to his wife and children for their patience, especially during the final stages of work on the book, and to Patricia L. Wheeler for her able secretarial help in preparation of the manuscript. Finally, for the help and encouragement given by associates, present and past, acknowledgement and thanks are sincerely proffered.

The George Washington University F.D.A.
January 1960

CONTENTS

Essentials of Human Embryology

Introduction, Adult Genital Organs, Gametogenesis

I. Introduction

A. Historical–To consider all of the many contributions made to the science of embryology is beyond the scope of this book. Nevertheless, it is essential to cite briefly the highlights of embryological investigation through the ages in order to establish a proper historical perspective.

1. *Aristotle* (4th century B.C.)–In any history of basic science Aristotle will be mentioned as having contributed much in many areas; he is, indeed, generally acknowledged to be the father of embryology. Despite the limitations imposed by lack of magnification he made many significant observations on the development of lower forms, especially the chick. He considered but rejected the idea of preformation and concluded the embryo developed from an amorphous mass, i.e. the embryo developed from activated menstrual blood.

2. *Harvey* and *Malpighi* (17th century), *Wolff* (18th century), *Pander* and *Schwann* (19th century)–These are names familiar to the history of embryology and, with many others, made numerous contributions to factual and theoretical aspects of the science.

3. *Von Baer* (19th century)–The work of this man has earned him the right to be called the "father of modern embryology" for his many contributions, including determination of the origins of the major organs, studies of comparative embryology, and the identification of the mammalian ovum. He also enlarged upon the significance of germ layers which had been described earlier (in the chick) by Pander.

4. Refinement and organization of the subject were accomplished by *Balfour, His, Keibel, Mall*, and others in the latter part of the 19th century and in the early 20th.

5. *Roux, Spemann, Harrison*, and *Morgan* introduced techniques of experimental embryology around the turn of the century that made possible the proof of theoretical and descriptive embryology.

6. *Streeter, Corner*, and others of the Carnegie Institution of Washington have done much to elucidate all areas of the subject. The Institution's investigations into primate and human materials are especially noteworthy. Similar acknowledgment should be made of the contributions of *Hertig* and *Rock* for their acquisition and study of the early stages of human embryonic material.

B. Divisions of embryology

1. Descriptive (morphological)–This division limits its consideration to the changes in form, structure, and relationships of organs and tissues of the developing embryo. It is the study of the anatomy of development. The bulk of this book is devoted to an exposition of this division.

2. Experimental embryology–This division considers the forces and influences that lead to the morphologic and physiologic changes in the embryo and attempts to elucidate such changes by experimental methods.

3. Developmental physiology–This division concerns itself with the study of the changes in the physiology of the developing embryo and fetus. It is an area in which much is yet to be discovered.

4. Abnormal development–This division regards the irregularities of development that lead to the appearance of malformations or anomalous conditions in the embryo and fetus. A synonym for this study is teratology.

C. Definition of common terms.

1. *Conceptus*–This is the product of conception which includes the embryo and its enveloping membranes.

2. *Embryo*–This is the designation for the developing organism from the end of the first week to the end of the second lunar month.

3. *Fetus*–This designates the organism between the end of the second lunar month and term, or birth.

4. *Growth*–This is the result of an increase in size or mass which may be due to a number of processes:

   a. *auxetic growth*–Due to the increase in size of cells

   b. *multiplicative growth*–Due to the increase in numbers of cells

   c. *differential growth*–Considers the growth of one part or area in comparison with growth in related or other parts

4

5. *Differentiation*-This is the process by which cells acquire or modify their characteristics, leading, thereby, to the establishment of new types of cells and tissues.

6. *Morphogenesis*-This is the process of development that leads to the establishment of form, e.g. morphogenetic movement is a movement of cells that will take part in the formation of a germ layer, tissue, or organ.

D. Importance of the study of embryology

1. Background for the understanding of other disciplines. Few if any subjects in the medical curriculum fail to find considerable support from a thorough understanding of embryology.

a. gross anatomical relationships are best explained by considering them in their simplest form within the embryo

b. histogenetic relationships between different tissues are made clear by consideration of them during their differentiation from simple germ layers.

c. pathology, especially that segment devoted to teratology, is elucidated by a knowledge of normal development. The study of neoplasms has considerable recourse to the fundamentals of histogenesis.

d. physiological studies are aided by the understanding of structures and function of the embryo and fetus.

2. Background for research is offered by the study of development. Scarcely any area of current research is not abetted by a knowledge of the fundamental processes of development.

II. · Adult Genital Organs

No attempt will be made to describe these organs in detail. The following descriptions are made merely to establish the sites at which the germ cell is produced, fertilization occurs, and subsequent development of the conceptus is achieved.

A. Male (Figs. 1, 3A)

1. *Testis*-This gland is the source of the male germ cell and is located in the *scrotal sac*. It is ovoid and consists of a great many *seminiferous tubules* within compartments formed by septa of the capsule (*tunica albuginea*) of the organ. The seminiferous tubules communicate with the *rete testis* in the *mediastinum* of the testis.

2. *Ductus epididymidis*-This is a highly coiled tubule which drains the rete testis via a system of collecting or *efferent ductules*.

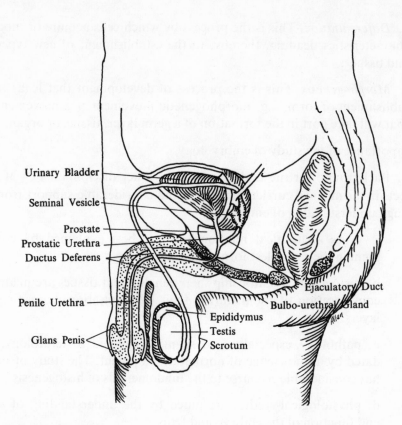

Urinary Bladder

Seminal Vesicle

Prostate
Prostatic Urethra
Ductus Deferens

Penile Urethra

Glans Penis

Ejaculatory Duct
Bulbo-urethral Gland

Epididymus
Testis
Scrotum

FIGURE **1.** Male reproductive system.

3. *Ductus (vas) deferens*–This is a muscular duct which is continuous with the ductus epididymidis and passes from the scrotum into the pelvic cavity where it terminates, via a specialized *ejaculatory duct,* in the prostatic urethra.

4. *Urethra*–This structure serves as the channel by which the urinary bladder is drained and consists of three portions: the *prostatic* (joined by the ejaculatory duct), *membranous,* and *spongy.*

5. Accessory organs–These structures consist of outgrowths of the genital tract which take part in the elaboration of secretions that comprise the semen.

a. *seminal vesicles*–Paired organs which join the terminal ends of each vas deferens.

b. *prostate*–This organ surrounds the intrapelvic portion of the urethra and secretes prostatic fluid into the latter by numerous small ducts.

c. *bulbo-urethral (Cowper's) glands*–These open into the membranous urethra and secrete a pre-ejaculatory fluid.

6

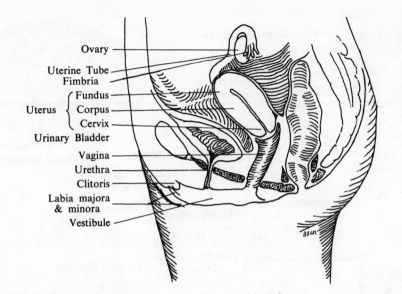

FIGURE **2.** Female reproductive system.

B. Female (Figs. 2, 3F)

1. *Ovary*–This gland produces the female germ cells or *ova*. It is ovoid and lies in the pelvis. It is covered by germinal epithelium and is intimately associated with the:

2. *Uterine (Fallopian) tubes*–The tubes open into the peritoneal cavity via the *ostia* which are surrounded by the finger-like *fimbria*. They are lined by ciliated epithelium which, aided by peristaltic action of the muscular wall, moves the ovum toward the:

3. *Uterus*–This is a hollow pear-shaped organ which is joined by the uterine tubes on either side. It is divided into the *fundus, body,* and the *cervix.* Its wall is divided into three layers:

   a. *endometrium*–Innermost, this layer lines the cavity of the uterus.

   b. *myometrium*–The muscular (smooth or involuntary muscle) layer which constitutes the major portion of the wall.

   c. *perimetrium (serosa)*–The peritoneal covering of the uterus.

4. *Vagina*–This is a hollow, tubular organ which receives the cervix of the uterus at its internal end and opens into the vestibule externally.

5. *Vestibule*–This is a depressed area between the *labia* or *vulvae* which is bounded posteriorly by the *posterior commissure* (fusion of labia majora caudally). The urethra and vagina open into it anteriorly and posteriorly respectively.

7

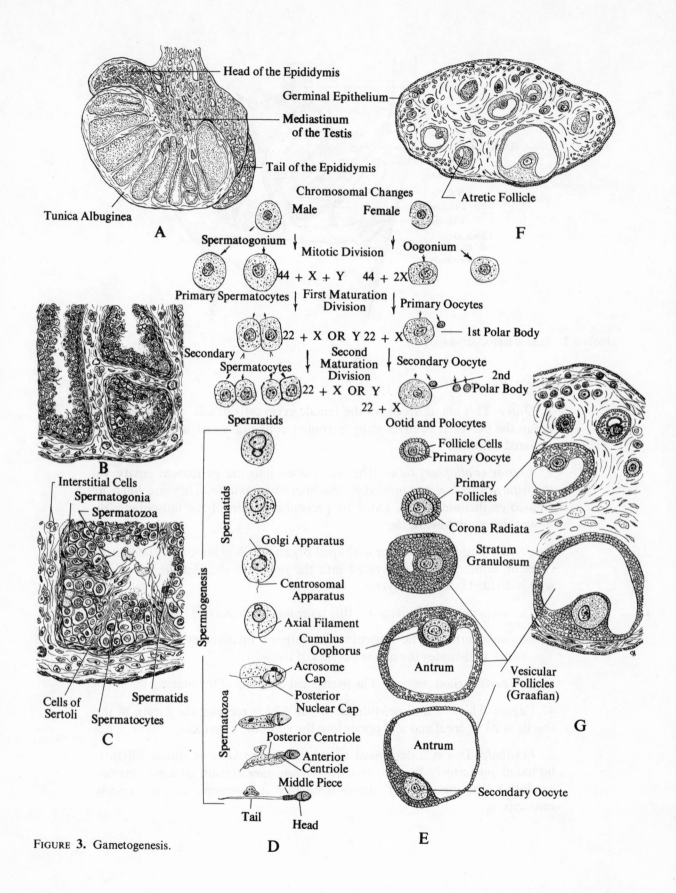

Head of the Epididymis

Germinal Epithelium

Mediastinum
of the Testis

Tail of the Epididymis

Tunica Albuginea

A

Atretic Follicle

F

Chromosomal Changes
Male   Female

Spermatogonium   Oogonium

Mitotic Division

44 + X + Y   44 + 2X

Primary Spermatocytes   First Maturation
Division

Primary Oocytes

22 + X OR Y 22 + X   1st Polar Body

Secondary   Second
Spermatocytes   Maturation
Division

Secondary Oocyte

22 + X OR Y   2nd
Polar Body

22 + X

Spermatids   Ootid and Polocytes

Follicle Cells
Primary Oocyte

Primary
Follicles

Corona Radiata

Golgi Apparatus   Stratum
Granulosum

Centrosomal
Apparatus

Axial Filament
Cumulus
Oophorus

Acrosome
Cap

Antrum   Vesicular
Follicles
(Graafian)

Posterior
Nuclear Cap

Posterior Centriole

Anterior
Centriole

Middle Piece

Antrum

Tail   Head

Secondary Oocyte

D   **E**

G

B

Interstitial Cells
Spermatogonia
Spermatozoa

Spermatids

Cells of   Spermatocytes
Sertoli

C

Spermiogenesis

Spermatids

Spermatozoa

FIGURE **3.** Gametogenesis.

III. Gametogenesis

This is the process of germ cell formation. (Figs. 3A, B, C, D)

A. *Spermatogenesis*

1. Definition–This is the process that results in the formation of the male germ cell or *spermatozoon.*

2. Site–The process occurs in the seminiferous tubules of the testis.

3. Occurrence–As a whole, the process occurs more or less continuously from puberty to senescence. However, at any given time during this period some of the tubules are actively engaged in the process whereas others are temporarily quiescent.

4. Features of process–Presumably *primordial germ cells* in the wall of the seminiferous tubules differentiate into a series of cells which will ultimately form the definitive male germ cell. The first or stem cell of this series is the:

   a. *spermatogonium*–This cell has the diploid chromosome number (44 somatic plus 2 sex).[1] It undergoes repeated mitotic division to give rise to many:

   b. *primary spermatocytes*–Like its parent cell, the primary spermatocyte is located just within the peripheral layer of the tubule. After enlarging the cell divides meiotically, giving rise to two daughter cells, the:

   c. *secondary spermatocytes*–These cells are smaller, are located nearer the lumen of the tubule, and have the haploid number of chromosomes (22 plus the X or Y sex chromosome). They undergo mitosis to form the:

   d. *spermatids*–These are cells with a haploid number of chromosomes which undergo the process of *spermiogenesis* or transformation into the definitive male gamete. This occurs as the spermatid is engulfed, to a greater or lesser degree, by the cytoplasm of the *Sertoli cells* in the wall of the tubule.

   e. *spermatozoa* (*sperm*)–This is the definitive germ cell produced by the transformation of the spermatid into a motile cell consisting of head, middle piece, and tail. The head is formed primarily by the nucleus

[1]The bulk of recent findings indicates that only 46 chromosomes are to be found in the nuclei of human cells in contrast to the number 48 which has been cited in most texts.

FIGURE 3. Gametogenesis. The process of spermatogenesis is represented on the left side of the drawing which shows a longitudinal section of the testis at A and drawings at increasing magnification at B and C which demonstrate the seminiferous tubules and interstitial tissues. The column of cells at D represents diagrammatically the process of spermatogenesis and spermiogenesis. Oögenesis is similarly represented at E and a longitudinal section of the ovary is represented at F and a portion of that section under higher magnification at G. (Drawing by Constance Herdeck. From *The Endocrinology of Reproduction* edited by J. T. Velardo, Oxford University Press, 1958.)

whereas the middle piece is formed by the centrosomal apparatus and remnants of the cytoplasm. The tail consists of an axial filament derived from the centrosomal apparatus and a delicate cytoplasmic sheath.

5. Fate of the spermatozoa–After their transformation, these cells are clustered around the tips of the cells of Sertoli which project into the lumen and are a source of nourishment for the sperm. Ultimately, the sperm are released and float free in the lumen of the seminiferous tubule, then pass through the rete testis and efferent ducts into the ductus epididymidis where *physiological maturation* occurs. From this point, they are carried through the vas deferens to the ampulla where they await ejaculation. If this does not occur they die and are absorbed. If sperm are deposited by ejaculation into the vagina they move rapidly into the uterus and uterine tubes. Their fertilizing ability is probably lost after 48 hours and the sperm dead in 96 hours.

6. *Semen* or *seminal fluid*–This is a complex mixture of substances, including spermatozoa, from the testis, seminal vesicle, and prostate, which provides a medium for the transport and nutrition of the spermatozoa.

B. *Oogenesis* (Figs. 3E, F, G)

1. Definition–This is the process of formation of the definitive female germ cell (ovum).

2. Site–This process occurs in the cortical portion of the ovary.

3. Occurrence–The process occurs from puberty (11-14 years) to menopause (at 40-50 years of age). It is cyclic in nature in nonpregnant women but is interrupted during pregnancy and, to a lesser degree, lactation.

4. Features of the process–Two features of this process involve the ovum proper and the surrounding cells that make up the follicle.

a. development of the follicle–The earliest indication of follicular development is the formation of simple clusters of cells in the periphery of the cortex which are probably derived from the germinal epithelium. The central cell of the cluster grows and becomes an *oogonium;* then, after more growth, becomes the *primary oocyte.* The remaining cells of the cluster form cuboidal *follicular cells,* and the entire structure is known as the:

(1) *primary follicle*–The follicle and contained oocyte increase in size and the follicular cells become more numerous, eventually multilayered. A homogeneous membrane (*zona pellucida*) develops around the oocyte and a cavity (*antrum*) is formed between follicular cells on one side of the oocyte. The cavity expands, the oocyte is

eccentrically placed on one side of the follicle, and the latter is called a:

(2) *vesicular* (*ovarian or graafian*) *follicle*–The cavity or antrum is filled with the liquor folliculi which contains estrogenic hormones. To this point the follicle has moved centripetally in the ovary but now reverses itself and approaches the surface of the ovary through which the oocyte is extruded at *ovulation.*

(3) *atretic follicles*–Many follicles begin development, become vesicular, and approach maturity. However, one of the follicles reaches the degree of maturity necessary for ovulation slightly before the others. When the mature follicle releases the oocyte at ovulation, the release of follicle stimulating hormone (F. S. H.) from the pituitary is inhibited and the other follicles degenerate by a process known as atresia.

b. development of the ovum

(1) *oogonium*–As noted above, this cell is derived from the primordial sex cell which has the diploid number of chromosomes (44 plus 2X). It enlarges and is surrounded by flattened, then cuboidal, follicular cells. When the latter is accomplished, i.e. when a primary follicle is established, the oogonium becomes the:

(2) *primary oocyte*–This cell continues to enlarge coincident with enlargement of the follicle. Within the vesicular follicle it is surrounded by follicular cells which form the *cumulus oophorus.* After ovulation the cells, clustered about the oocyte, are known as the *corona radiata.* As the vesicular follicle matures, the primary oocyte (having 44 plus 2X chromosomes) undergoes a meiotic division which results in the production of the haploid first *polar body* and the:

(3) *secondary oocyte*–This cell also contains the haploid number of chromosomes (22 plus 1X) but receives virtually all of the cytoplasm of its precursor. Almost immediately following its formation, the secondary oocyte initiates a mitotic division and it is at this point that it is released from the follicle, i.e. ovulation occurs.

If fertilization does not occur within 24-36 hours following ovulation, the oocyte dies. If fertilized, it completes the mitotic division yielding a second small polar body and becomes the:

(4) *fertilized ootid* or *ovum* (*zygote*)–The unfertilized ootid or ovum probably never exists in reality. Polar bodies have no known function in addition to the passive role they play in meiosis, i.e. reduction of chromosome number.

11

2

Ovulation, Fertilization, and Implantation

I. **Ovulation (Figs. 4, 5)**

A. Definition–Ovulation is the release of the mature ovum from the graafian follicle, a process occurring once about every 28 days in the human female between puberty (at about the 14th year) and menopause (at about the 45th year) unless interrupted by pregnancy or pathological conditions.

B. Associated processes–Ovulation is correlated with and, in part, responsible for certain changes in the genital tract and ovary designed essentially to prepare the uterus for the reception and maintenance of the fertilized ovum. These changes involve the uterine mucosa and the ovary especially. Changes in the latter are responsible for proliferation and modification of the uterine mucosa which make it able to support the implanting ovum or, if implantation does not occur, to shed the inner mucosa and begin the process anew.

Changes in the mucosa are cyclic and constitute the:

1. Menstrual cycle–This cycle is arbitrarily divided into several phases or stages.

a. *menses* or *menstruation*–This phase of the cycle is characterized by a shedding of the superficial layers of the uterine mucosa with coincident bleeding and discharge from the vagina of the blood and tissue shed. It lasts from three to five days. (Fig. 4)

b. *repair* and *proliferation*–This stage is characterized by repair of the denuded mucosa, increase in thickness of the mucosa, and establishment of the straight uterine glands. This stage requires about 10 days. (Fig. 4)

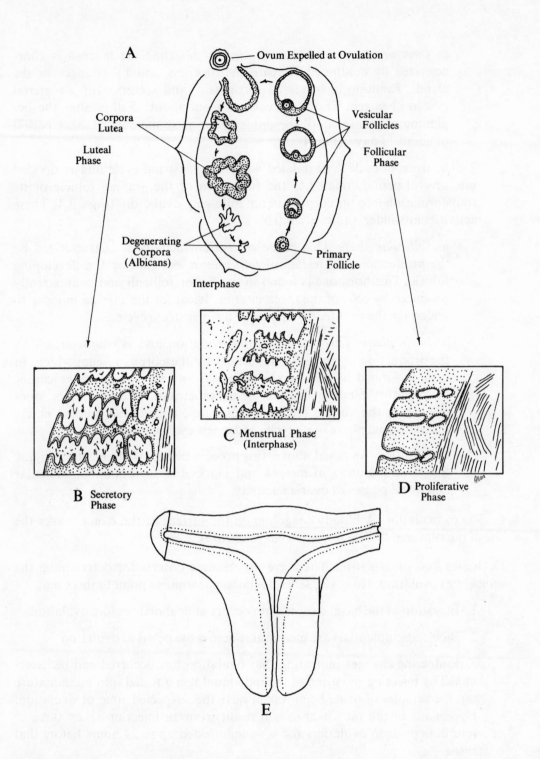

A — Ovum Expelled at Ovulation

Corpora
Lutea

Luteal
Phase

Vesicular
Follicles

Follicular
Phase

Degenerating
Corpora
(Albicans)

Primary
Follicle

Interphase

B Secretory
Phase

C Menstrual Phase
(Interphase)

D Proliferative
Phase

E

FIGURE **4.** Correlation of ovulatory and menstrual cycles. The ovary is shown at A and the ovulatory cycle diagrammatically represented within. B, C, and D are diagrammatic representations of the uterine endometrium (from a position noted at E) at characteristic moments during the menstrual cycle.

c. *secretory* or *premenstrual phase*–At this time the mucosa is characterized by continued increase in thickness and by changes in the glands, resulting in increased tortuousity and secretion of a material rich in glycogen. This stage extends from about 15 days after the beginning of menses until the onset of the next menses or for a period of about 13 days. (Fig. 4)

2. The ovarian cycle is correlated with the menstrual cycle and is divided into several periods related to the formation of the graffian follicle or its transformation into the corpus luteum following ovulation. (Figs. 3,4) These activities are under pituitary control.

a. *follicular phase*–This phase of ovarian activity is characterized by the production and release of *folliculin* or *estradiol* by the developing follicle. This hormone is found in the liquor folliculi and is apparently produced by cells of the theca interna. It causes the uterine mucosa to undertake the proliferative phase of the menstrual cycle.

b. *luteal phase*–This phase follows ovulation and is characterized by the production of *progestin* elaborated by the corpus luteum which, in turn, is formed by cells of the collapsed follicle. The hormone causes the secretory phase of the uterine endometrium. If implantation does not occur, the corpus luteum degenerates, the uterine mucosa enters the menstrual phase of its cycle, and a new cycle is begun.

c. *ovulation*–As noted above, this process occurs at about the 14th day following the onset of menses and marks the separation of follicular and luteal phases of ovarian activity.

C. Site of ovulation–A bloody coagulum on the surface of the ovary marks the site of the ruptured follicle (*corpus hemorrhagicum*).

D. Indications of ovulation–There are no absolute criteria for determining the moment of ovulation. However, several related phenomena point to this event.

1. Elevation of the basal temperature occurs at or shortly before ovulation.

2. Bioelectric potentials are measurable across the pelvis at ovulation.

3. Endocrine changes indicating that ovulation has occurred can be determined by injecting the urine of the individual being tested into an immature rat, the samples of urine being taken near the suspected time of ovulation. Hyperemia of the rat's ovaries will result from an injection taken three to four days prior to ovulation and is so manifested up to 24 hours before that event.

4. Examination of vaginal smears, cervical mucus, and vaginal pH all have been used with variable success in determining the time of ovulation.

14

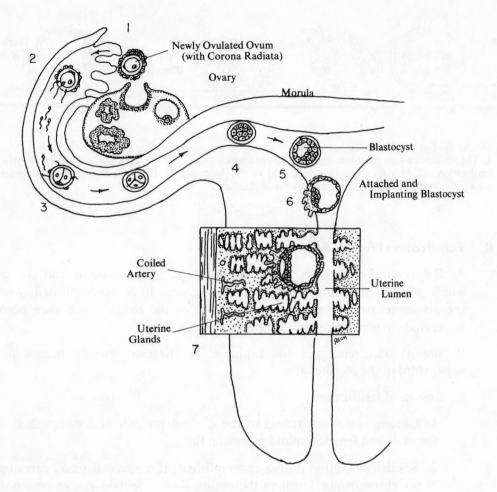

Newly Ovulated Ovum
(with Corona Radiata)

Ovary

Morula

Blastocyst

Attached and
Implanting Blastocyst

Coiled
Artery

Uterine
Lumen

Uterine
Glands

FIGURE 5. Ovulation and fate of conceptus. The ovum at ovulation (1) is picked up by the uterine tube, fertilized by a spermatozoon (within 12–24 hours) (2) where it becomes a zygote. The zygote undergoes cleavage (3) to form the morula (4) which enters the uterine cavity (4–5 days after fertilization) where it then becomes a blastocyst (5), initiates implantation (6) (at late day 6 or early day 7), and completes implantation at (7) (on day 11).

E. Fate of the discharged ovum (Fig. 5)

1. In the peritoneal cavity momentarily, the egg is soon picked up by the fimbria of the uterine tube and is carried through the lumen of the latter toward the uterus.

2. When fertilization occurs it is usually in the upper third of the uterine tube.

3. If the ovum is not fertilized (it is probably viable for about 24 hours) it dies and is lost in the uterine secretions.

15

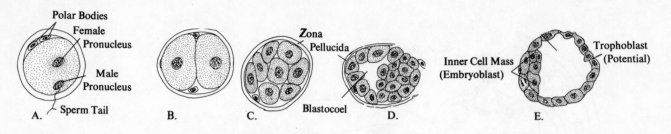

FIGURE **6.** Early stages of the conceptus.
A. The fertilized ovum (becomes zygote when pronuclei fuse).   B. Two-cell stage appears shortly after fertilization. C. Morula about the fourth day of development. D. Early blastocyst. Note degenerating zona pellucida. E. Older blastocyst ready for implantation.

II.   Fertilization (Figs. 5,6A)

A. Definition–Fertilization is the union of the spermatozoon and the ovum which results in the formation of the *zygote.* It is accomplished when a spermatozoon penetrates the zona pellucida of the ovum which then becomes impervious to penetration by additional spermatozoa.

B. Site of occurrence–As noted above, fertilization usually occurs in the upper third of the uterine tube.

C. Results of fertilization

1. Chromosomal restitution to the diploid number is accomplished when the male and female haploid pronuclei fuse.

2. Sex determination is also accomplished. If a spermatozoon carrying the X sex chromosome fertilizes the ovum, then a female zygote results from the union. If the spermatozoon carries the Y sex chromosome, a male zygote is formed.

3. Initiation of cleavage or a series of rapid mitotic cell divisions is an additional resultant of fertilization. By such cell division the large zygote is reduced to a number of smaller, more workable cells.

D. Movements of the fertilized zygote–(Let it be noted here that until recently it has been the practice to refer to the zygote and subsequent forms of the conceptus as the ovum. This will not be the practice of this book and the appropriate term will be used whenever possible.) Following fertilization the conceptus is carried into the lumen of the uterus. This requires about five days.

E. Changes in the zygote are the result of cleavage which leads to the formation of the two-cell, four-cell, six-cell, etc., stages of the organism. The individual cells are called blastomeres and at the end of four days the blastomeres form:

1. The *morula,* which consists of a solid cluster of blastomeres (Figs. 5, 6C)

16

2. The *blastula* or *blastocyst* is formed when the morula becomes enlarged and hollowed out. It is the blastocyst which reaches the uterine lumen at the fifth day. (Figs. 6D, E)

III. Implantation of the Blastula (Fig. 5)

A. Definition–Implantation is the process by which the free-floating blastula attaches to and penetrates the superficial layers of the uterine endometrium.

B. Site of implantation–A brief description of the uterine endometrium will aid in the orientation of the implanting blastocyst. The endometrium consists of three layers:

1. *Stratum compactum*–This layer lies next to the uterine lumen and has a layer of simple columnar epithelium through which the uterine glands penetrate. The connective tissue between the glands and under the epithelium is quite compact as compared to deeper layers.

2. *Stratum spongiosum*–This layer lies beneath the compactum and consists essentially of the dilated, tortuous middle portions of the uterine glands and the intervening connective tissue.

3. *Stratum basale*–This is the outermost of the layers and is intimately associated with the inner surface of the myometrium or uterine muscle. It consists of the basal portions of the glands, arterioles, venules, etc.

Implantation proper takes place within the stratum compactum and is usually on the posterior wall of the fundus of the uterus.

C. Time following ovulation–Implantation is begun on about the seventh day and completed about the eleventh day following ovulation and fertilization.

D. The actual process of implantation is accomplished by the following steps: (see Figs. 7A, B)

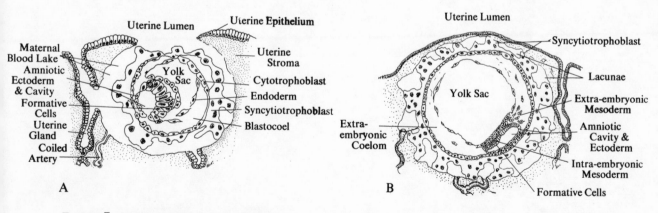

FIGURE 7. Implantation and early embryology.
A. Early implantation (defect in epithelium of endometrium still apparent). B. Implantation completed.

17

1. Disappearance of the zona pellucida.

2. Attachment of blastula to the epithelial layer of the stratum compactum.

3. Penetration of the epithelium and superficial layers of the stratum compactum by the blastula follows with a disruption of uterine vessels and glands in the area penetrated. The debris and extravasated blood form the *embryotrophe*, which is available for the nourishment of the conceptus.

4. Closure of the penetration defect by a coagulum then occurs and is followed by epithelial repair.

5. Invasion of the uterine stroma by the blastocyst and enlargement of its outer layer (*trophoblast*) occurs and a differentiation of layers derived from the trophoblast is then accomplished:

    a. outer *syncytiotrophoblast*

    b. inner *cytotrophoblast*

6. Invasion of the syncytiotrophoblast into the uterine stroma occurs with the formation of *lacunae* in the syncytiotrophoblast and a *decidual reaction* of the uterine cells, which it contacts.

E. Abnormal sites of implantation are not infrequently found, especially in the following areas: uterine tube (tubal), uterine tube as it passes through the uterine wall (interstitial), peritoneum, and ovary. The implantation may be relatively successful and the conceptus maintained for extended periods. These are called *ectopic* pregnancies and are usually terminated by rupture and hemorrhage.

18

3

Early Embryology, The Presomite Embryo (Germ Layer

Formation), and Twinning

I.   Early Embryology (Fig. 6)

A. *Zygote*-As observed in the previous chapter the zygote is formed by the union of the pronuclei of the male and female gametes. When this occurs, the zygote is still surrounded by the zona pellucida and is in the upper portion of the uterine tube. As it is carried toward the uterus, cleavage or repeated mitotic cell division occurs, resulting in the formation of an increasing number of smaller cells or blastomeres.

B. *Morula*-This describes the cluster of blastomeres resulting from cleavage, and consists of an outer layer of cells surrounding an inner group of cells. By this time (4–5 days postovulation) the conceptus or morula has traversed the tube and has reached the uterine cavity (see Fig. 5). Fluid accumulates between one side of the *inner cell mass* and the outer layer, thus converting the morula into the:

C. *Blastula or blastocyst*-Increased accumulation of fluid enlarges the cavity (*blastocoel*) and causes the inner cell mass to be placed eccentrically. At this point the zona pellucida disintegrates and attachment, with subsequent implantation, is undertaken (Figs. 5,7)

   1. *Trophoblast*-This is the outer layer of the blastocyst which ultimately forms the bulk of the fetal membranes (*placenta*).

   2. *Inner cell mass* (embryoblast)-The inner group of blastomeres become located to one side of the blastocoel intimately associated with the overlying trophoblast. The embryo develops from the inner cell mass.

19

II. Presomite Embryo (Germ Layer Formation) (Figs. 7,8,9,10,11)

As noted above, the embryo develops from the inner cell mass. At first the latter consists of a simple layer of cells. Soon, however, a second layer appears on the internal aspect of the inner cell mass and constitutes the:

A. *Endoderm*–These cells extend beyond the margin of the inner cell mass, indeed, over the internal aspect of the trophoblast, forming thereby a sack, the *primary yolk sac,* within the blastula. The inner cell mass is converted into a bilaminar plate, the embryonic disc, by the formation of the endoderm. The cells of the inner cell mass that remain between endoderm and trophoblast become the:

B. *Formative cells* (ectoderm in older terminology)–These cells will give rise to both *ectoderm* and *mesoderm.* At the margin of the embryonic disc the formative cells are continuous with cells which are derived from the trophoblast and which line the roof of the *amniotic cavity.* The latter appears between the formative cells and overlying trophoblast. The cells lining the roof of the amniotic cavity constitute the *amniotic ectoderm.*

C. *Extra-embryonic mesoderm*–These cells appear between the trophoblast and the primary yolk sac and apparently are derived from the former. Proliferation of the mesodermal cells forms a loose network of cells, the *magma reticulare,* which eventually splits and forms a cavity, the *extra-embryonic coelom,* in the interval. The mesoderm associated with the yolk sac is called *splanchnic mesoderm* whereas that associated with the trophoblast becomes known as the *chorionic mesoderm.* (Fig. 8)

D. *Intra-embryonic mesoderm*–Development to this point has resulted in the formation of a bilaminar disc located between the amniotic cavity and the yolk

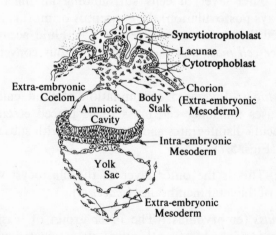

FIGURE **8.** Early embryology. Cross section of embryonic disc. (Note particularly the changes in the embryonic disc and chorion.)

20

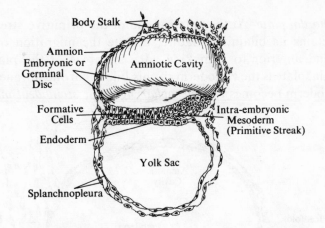

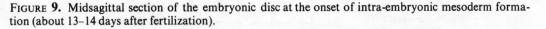

FIGURE 9. Midsagittal section of the embryonic disc at the onset of intra-embryonic mesoderm formation (about 13–14 days after fertilization).

sac. The embryonic endoderm and formative cells (ectoderm) are continuous at the periphery of the disc with extra-embryonic (splanchnic) endoderm of the yolk sac and with the extra-embryonic (amniotic) ectoderm of the amniotic cavity respectively. At the edge of the disc an area of rapidly proliferating formative cells gives rise to the intra-embryonic mesoderm. This forms the *primitive streak*. Cells from the streak gain the interval between formative (now ectoderm) and endodermal layers and extend to the edge of the disc where they contact extra-embryonic mesoderm. This migration occurs in all directions. This is especially true caudally where the rapid proliferation and migration of these cells bring about an elongation of the disc. (Figs. 9,10)

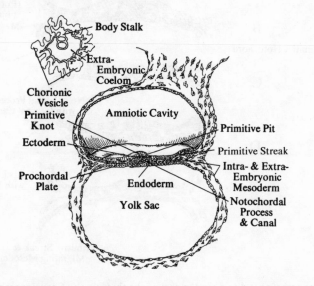

FIGURE 10. Midsagittal section of the embryonic disc at the onset of notochord formation. (Note the relative position of the embryonic disc in the insert at the upper left-hand side.)

E. *Prochordal plate*–At the anterior end of the primitive streak there is an area which retains its bilaminar nature, despite the migration of mesodermal cells lateral and anterior to it making adjacent areas of the plate trilaminar. The prochordal plate is the endoderm of this bilaminar membrane and with the overlying ectoderm becomes the *buccopharyngeal* or *stomodeal membrane*. (Figs. 10, 11)

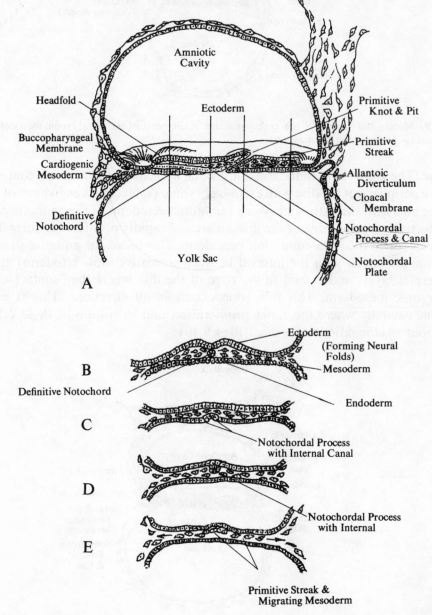

FIGURE 11. The embryonic disc near the end of the third week of development (late presomite embryo). Midsagittal section of the embryonic disc at A with cross sections B, C, D, and E taken from the points indicated.

22

F. *Cloacal membrane*–A similar fusion of endoderm and ectoderm at the caudal end of the primitive streak constitutes this membrane. Mesoderm extending caudally and fusing with the mesoderm of the body stalk does so by passing around the cloacal membrane. (Fig. 11)

G. *Notochord formation*–Up to this point in development the embryonic disc has been elongating, with the prochordal plate, primitive streak, and the cloacal membrane forming an axis for this process. To the embryo an axial supporting element is now added by the following means. (Figs. 10,11,12)

1. *Primitive knot* (*Hensen's node*)–This is an area of rapidly proliferating formative cells in midline at the anterior extremity of the primitive streak. Cells from this area migrate, or are pushed by the multiplicative efforts of adjacent cells, into the interval between ectoderm and endoderm. In so doing they form the:

2. *Primitive pit* (blastopore)–This pit appears at the site at which the cells noted above invaginate. From the pit a cord of cells is formed which extends forward to the prochordal plate. This is the:

3. *Notochordal process*–The cord is later hollowed out by the *notochordal canal* (which later becomes the *archenteric,* then *neurenteric canal*) and increases in length due to a caudal migration of the primitive knot and an addition of cells, therefore, to the caudal end of the notochordal process.

4. *Notochordal plate*–The notochordal process intercalates itself between endodermal cells in the roof of the yolk sac and at the same time flattens out. This allows the notochordal canal to communicate with the yolk sac; at this point the canal is known as the archenteric canal. Later the plate reforms

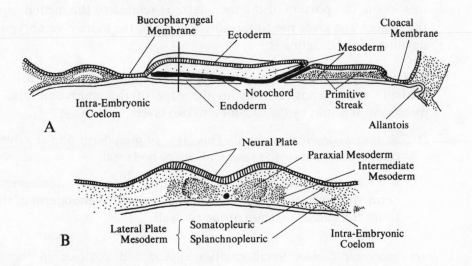

FIGURE 12. Division of the intra-embryonic mesoderm (late presomite embryo). A. Midsagittal section. B. Cross section at point indicated at A.

23

into a rod-like structure, regains its position between endoderm and ecto-derm in the midline, and is known as the:

5. *Definitive notochord*-This structure acts as the axial skeleton until re-placed by the permanent structures, i.e. vertebrae. (Figs. 11,12)

H. Craniocaudal gradient of development-The processes of primitive streak, mesoderm, and notochord formation result in the elongation of the embryo by the addition of more recently formed tissues to the caudal edge of the embryo. Hence, the later steps in each process are observed occuring at the cranial end of the embryo, whereas the initial and early steps are noted more caudally. Such a gradient of development is noticeable throughout the remainder of fetal life, i.e. structures at the cranial end of the embryo will be seen to be farther along in their development as compared to similar structures located more caudally.

I. Further development of intra-embryonic mesoderm-After its formation and extension between the layers of the embryonic disc, the mesoderm becomes dis-tributed in such a way as to necessitate further division and designation. (Fig. 12)

1. *Cardiogenic* mesoderm-This mesoderm migrates from the primitive streak to the midline anterior to the prochordal plate and ultimately gives rise to the heart.

2. *Paraxial* mesoderm-This is a thickened mass of mesoderm which lies immediately adjacent to the notochord and is eventually divided up into the bilateral *somites*.

3. *Intermediate* mesoderm-Continuous with and just lateral to the paraxial mesoderm, this portion of the mesoderm is related to the medial aspect of the coelom and gives rise to the adrenal cortex, the kidneys (embryonic and definitive), and the gonads.

4. *Lateral plate* mesoderm-This tissue is continuous with the former medially and extends laterally to the edge of the embryonic disc in all directions. It is split by the coelom into two layers:

a. *somatopleuric* mesoderm-This layer of mesoderm and the overlying ectoderm constitute the *somatopleura* or body wall.

b. *splanchnopleuric* mesoderm-In contrast to the somatopleuric meso-derm, this layer of mesoderm, with the associated endoderm of the gut, forms the *splanchnopleura* or the gut wall.

J. *Intra-embryonic coelom*-Small cavities appear and coalesce in the lateral plate mesoderm. Eventually a large, U-shaped cavity is formed which surrounds the axial portions of the embryo. (Fig. 13) The connection between the lateral

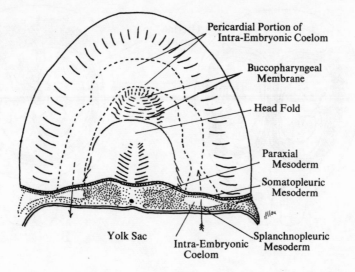

Pericardial Portion of
Intra-Embryonic Coelom

Buccopharyngeal
Membrane

Head Fold

Paraxial
Mesoderm

Somatopleuric
Mesoderm

Yolk Sac

Intra-Embryonic
Coelom

Splanchnopleuric
Mesoderm

FIGURE **13.** Early intra-embryonic coelom in a presomite embryo. Anterior half of embryo viewed from dorsal and posterior. The intra-embryonic coelom indicated by dotted lines.

coelomic cavities is found anterior to the prochordal plate and is therefore intimately associated with cardiogenic mesoderm. This portion of the coelom is destined to become the *pericardial* cavity whereas its caudal extensions form the *pleuro-peritoneal* cavities. The caudalmost portion of the latter usually communicates with the extra-embryonic coelom due to a failure of fusion of the somatopleura and splanchnopleura laterally. The extra-embryonic coelom is that space between the inner layer of the trophoblast and the yolk sac and amnionic membranes. It is ultimately obliterated by the expansion of the amniotic cavity and its contents.

III. Twinning—Multiple Births

It seems logical to pause here for a brief consideration of the factors involved in, or responsible for, the simultaneous formation of multiple embryos. The number of such multiple births ranges from two to six. Twins, by far the most common, occur approximately once in 86 births with triplets and quadruplets decreasing in frequency logarithmically. Two types of twins can be distinguished. (Fig. 14)

A. *Dizygotic* (*fraternal*) *twins*–Both individuals are the product of separate eggs. That is, two eggs are released and fertilized, resulting in two siblings of the same or opposite sex resembling each other to the same degree as siblings from single births. More than two eggs fertilized would result in *polyzygotic* births.

25

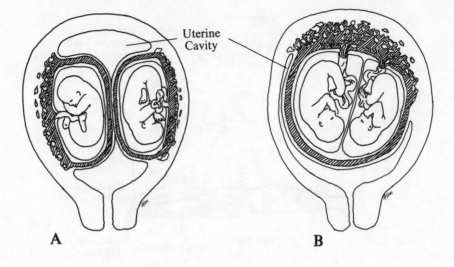

FIGURE 14. Fetal membranes and placenta in twinning.
A. Dizygotic (fraternal) twins. Note separation of fetal membranes and placentae.
B. Monozygotic (identical) twins. Both within a single chorionic sac but with separate amnionic membranes.

B. *Monozygotic* (*identical*) *twins*-In this case, both individuals are derived from the same fertilized ovum, hence, have the identical chromosomal or genetic make-up. They will be the same sex and very much alike in appearance. Several explanations of this situation exist. It is thought that the early formation of a doubled inner cell mass or a splitting of the embryonic disc are the most likely explanations for identical twinning. The embryos are contained in a single chorionic sac in both cases (Fig. 14B), and in the latter instance they share a single amnionic sac. Separation of the early blastomeres in lower forms leads to the formation of monozygotic twins but this is not thought to be a factor in human twinning due to the presence of the unyielding zona pellucida.

C. *Conjoined* (*Siamese*) *twins*-If separation of the inner cell mass or embryonic disc is delayed or incomplete, embryos which are fused to a greater or lesser degree result. Such fusion occurs along the midline.

26

4

Placentation, Fetal Membranes

I. Introduction

The consideration of placentation and the development of fetal membranes should be prefaced by a brief study of the site at which these processes occur, i.e. the uterine endometrium. Implantation and subsequent placentation take place while the uterus is in its secretory phase of activity.

A. Uterine endometrium–This tissue lines the uterine cavity and consists of a surface epithelium (columnar) and the underlying connective tissue in which are glands, nutrient vessels, etc. It is divided into three layers: (Fig. 15)

1. *Stratum compactum*–This layer is next to the lumen of the uterus and includes, therefore, the epithelium and a rather compact connective tissue immediately subjacent. The latter is penetrated only by the necks of the uterine glands.

27

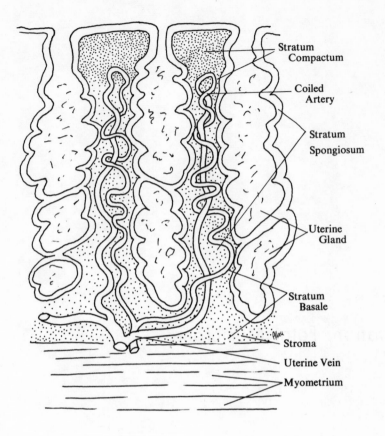

FIGURE **15.** Uterine endometrium, secretory (progestational) phase.

2. *Stratum spongiosum*–The presence of the tortuous uterine glands occupying the bulk of this layer gives it a spongy appearance. In this phase of activity the glands are loaded with secretions. Capillary loops extend into this layer.

3. *Stratum basale*–Intimately associated with the myometrium, this layer contains the bases of the uterine glands, the bases of the spiral arterioles, and a moderately compact stroma.

B. *Decidua*–When the blastula completes implantation and with establishment of the placenta, several changes in the structure and the relationships of the endometrium occur. The intimate association between the fetal chorion and the uterine endometrium necessitates the shedding of the latter with the fetal tissues at birth, hence its designation as the decidua. (Figs. 16,17)

28

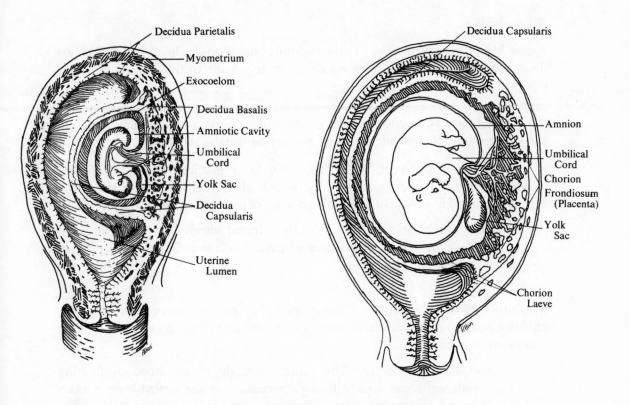

Decidua Parietalis
Myometrium
Exocoelom
Decidua Basalis
Amniotic Cavity
Umbilical Cord
Yolk Sac
Decidua Capsularis
Uterine Lumen

Decidua Capsularis
Amnion
Umbilical Cord
Chorion Frondiosum (Placenta)
Yolk Sac
Chorion Laeve

FIGURE **16.** The decidua, fetal membranes, and placenta (end of first month of development).

FIGURE **17.** The decidua, fetal membranes, and placenta (end of second month of development).

1. *Decidua basalis*–This is the endometrium between the conceptus or chorionic vesicle and the myometrium of the uterus, which becomes the maternal component of the placenta.

2. *Decidua capsularis*–Since implantation occurs in the stratum compactum, the chorionic vesicle is located near the lumen of the uterine cavity with only a thin layer of endometrium covering it. The latter becomes the decidua capsularis which expands coextensively with enlargement of the chorionic vesicle. As expansion occurs the decidua capsularis comes into apposition with, and fuses to, the remainder of the uterine endometrium, thus obliterating the uterine lumen.

3. *Decidua parietalis*–All of the endometrium with the exception of that noted above and that within the cervical canal constitutes the parietal decidua. This portion of the decidua fuses with the decidua capsularis and is compressed and flattened as the conceptus increases in size.

II.   Placentation

As the blastocyst invades the uterine endometrium its outer layer or trophoblast undergoes certain specialization which ultimately leads to the formation of the placenta and other fetal membranes.

A. Trophoblast–This is the source of the bulk of extra-embryonic tissue. In early stages of implantation two layers are distinguishable: (Figs. 7,8)

> 1. Syncytiotrophoblast–This is the outer layer in direct contact with maternal tissues. It is characterized by its lack of cellular separation, the nuclei being found in a sheet of cytoplasm devoid of intercellular boundaries.

> 2. Cytotrophoblast–This layer of cells is found internal to the former and retains, at least in the early stages of gestation, the individual integrity of its component cells.

B. *Chorion*–When formation of the extra-embryonic mesoderm from the trophoblast is completed, the latter membrane is converted into the chorion and the blastocyst into the:

> 1. *Chorionic vesicle* or *sac*–This structure might be described as floating in the *maternal blood lake,* although processes of the syncytiotrophoblast extend to and contact the maternal tissues on the margin of the "lake." The substances bathing the chorionic vesicle are the breakdown products of the invaded tissues, blood, glandular secretions, and tissue fluid. It is called the *embryotrophe.* The conceptus is maintained by nutrients from the embryotrophe which pass, at first, into the chorionic vesicle by simple diffusion. The chorionic vesicle enlarges and exhibits small finger-like processes which extend into the embryotrophe and maternal tissues. These are the:

> 2. Chorionic villi–The essential function of the villi is to increase the surface area of the chorionic vesicle available for the absorption of nutrients from the embryotrophe; later, the maternal blood. The villi are formed in three stages: (Fig. 18)

>> a. *primary villus*–this structure is formed when a process of syncytiotrophoblast is invaded by a core of cytotrophoblast.

>> b. *secondary villus*–this is formed when the core of cytotrophoblast is invaded by a secondary core of mesoderm.

>> c. *tertiary, definitive,* or *functional villus*–the development of blood vessels in the mesodermal core of the villus establishes the final stage of villus formation. However, thinning of the syncytiotrophoblast, virtual disappearance of the cytotrophoblast, and an accumulation of pigment in the former are to be noted in the villus of mid and late gestation.

3. *Chorion laeve*–At first the chorionic villi completely cover the chorionic sac. Later, however, that portion of the latter associated with the decidua capsularis becomes devoid of villi, hence, smooth.

4. *Chorion frondiosum*–On the other hand, the villi on the basal side of the sac increase in number and size and become modified to form the definitive placenta or placenta proper.

C. Placental circulation–Involved in this consideration are vessels within the chorion which conduct blood to and from the embryo or fetus and the source and the route taken by maternal blood which bathes the villi. (Figs. 18,19).

1. Fetal component–As will be described elsewhere in detail, simple vessels are formed, almost simultaneously, in the embryo, yolk sac, body stalk, and chorionic villi. These vessels become joined together forming a primitive circulation which links the embryo, by way of the body stalk, with the chorionic villi. Thus fetal blood is constantly passing through vessels within the villi, where exchange of substances with maternal blood can be accomplished.

2. Maternal component–This portion of placental circulation is derived from the:

a. primitive maternal blood lake–Formed by the erosion of maternal tissues and vessels by the implanting blastocyst. With only slight modifications this situation prevails with the maternal blood lake becoming converted into the:

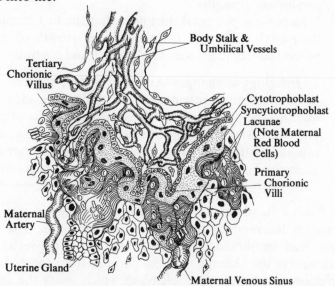

FIGURE **18.** The chorion in early stages of development. The syncytiotrophoblast is stippled. Note the decidual reaction (swelling) of stromal cells of the endometrium wherever contact with syncytiotrophoblast is made. The lacunae (intervillus spaces) are labyrinthine and contain maternal (non-nucleated) red blood cells. The fetal vessels, on the other hand, contain nucleated red blood cells.

31

b. intervillous spaces-Blood entering the intervillous space comes from the tapped or eroded ends of the spiral arterioles and filters peripherally into the:

c. marginal sinus-This is a specialized extension of the intervillous space which is drained by the uterine veins found at the periphery of the placenta. Partial septation or lobulation of the placenta further complicates the pattern somewhat but the general pattern remains.

It should be noted that the direction of flow of maternal blood is opposite to that of the fetal stream within the chorionic villus. This results in maximum efficiency of nutrient and gaseous exchange. That is to say, the transport or diffusion gradient of these substances is maintained throughout the entire length of their association on either side of the chorionic membrane.

D. Placental maturation (Fig. 19)

1. Gross changes-At the end of the first month of gestation the invasion of the chorion approaches the stratum basale of the endometrium. The circumscribed chorion frondiosum becomes converted into the discoid placenta. Certain of the larger chorionic villi act as anchors by fusing with the endometrium. Secondary and tertiary branches of the larger villi arise from the distal portions of the anchoring villi and grow toward the *chorionic plate,* i.e. toward the fetus. Septa with the same derivation also grow in the same direction and incompletely separate the placenta into smaller units called cotyledons. (Fig. 19)

Increase in placental thickness after the first month of gestation is due to the growth of the villi. Circumferential growth of the placenta is a gradual process concomitant with fetal growth and continues until term.

2. Histological changes-As noted above, the cytotrophoblast disappears, or becomes much attenuated and difficult to identify at about the fourth month. The syncytiotrophoblast also becomes attenuated but is retained and with a small amount of mesenchymal tissue and the endothelium of the capillary within the villus forms the placental barrier. The syncytiotrophoblast also becomes pigmented in later stages of gestation.

E. Fate of the placenta-At termination of pregnancy rupture of the fetal membranes is followed by the expulsion of the fetus. The decidua, placenta, and associated membranes (afterbirth) are usually delivered shortly thereafter. Detachment of the placenta and the decidua from the endometrium occurs by the development of a plane of cleavage which splits the stratum spongiosum and allows those structures to be delivered by the expulsive efforts of uterine contractions. Contraction of the uterine wall is such as to prevent excessive bleeding from the denuded endometrium.

Placenta praevia is a condition in which the placenta lies over the internal os of the uterine cervix. When labor starts in this condition, the placenta is expelled before the fetus with the obvious result of anoxia and possible death of the fetus.

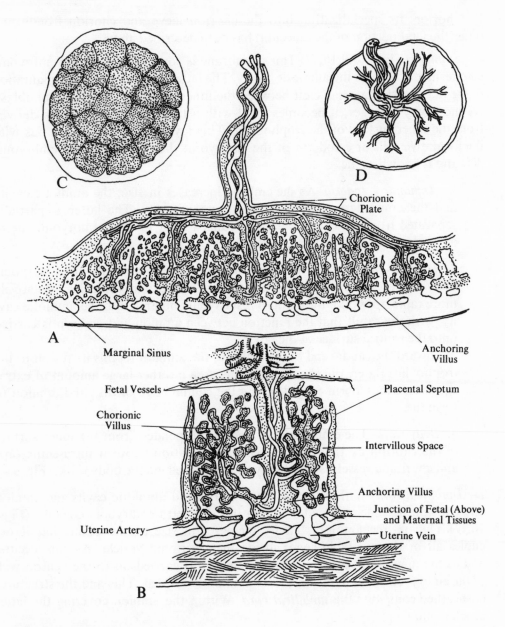

FIGURE **19.** The placenta.
A. The definitive placenta in cross section.
B. An enlargement of a segment of the cross section shown in A.
C. The placenta from the maternal side showing divisions into cotyledons.
D. The placenta from the fetal (amniotic) side showing the distribution of the umbilical vessels.

33

III. Fetal Membranes

A. Definition—Under this heading are usually grouped all the extra-embryonic structures, some of them membranes in a real sense—others not, derived from the primitive blastomeres.

B. Chorion—Its specialization into the chorion laeve and chorion frondiosum (later the fetal portion of the placenta) has been described above.

C. *Amnion*—(Figs. 7,8,9,16,17) This membrane is continuous with the embryonic ectoderm and bounds the amniotic cavity. The latter appears during implantation of the blastocyst as a small cleft between the inner cell mass and the trophoblast. As the cavity enlarges, it becomes lined with a layer of epithelial cells derived from the inner surface of the trophoblast. This layer of cells is continuous with the formative cells or ectoderm of the embryo at the margins of the embryonic disc and is known as the:

1. *Amnionic ectoderm*—As the embryo increases in size, the amniotic cavity and the amniotic ectoderm expand concomitantly. The latter is partially separated from the trophoblast and gains a layer of extra-embryonic mesoderm. In so doing it becomes the:

2. *Definitive amnion*—At first, the junction of amnion with the embryonic body wall is coextensive with the periphery of the embryonic disc. Relatively more rapid growth of the embryo results in its bulging into the amniotic cavity, with the result that the junction between amnion and embryo is carried onto the ventral surface of the latter.

Toward the caudal end of the embryo, the amnion retains its fusion to the trophoblast (later, the chorion). In this area a rather large amount of extra-embryonic mesoderm extends along the caudal edge of disc and amnion to form the:

3. *Body stalk*—The embryo is, in a sense, suspended from the inner surface of the chorion by this structure. Communication between intra-embryonic and chorionic vessels is eventually accomplished via the body stalk. (Fig. 9)

D. *Umbilical cord*—With growth of the embryo and amniotic cavity the amnion and chorion become apposed, obliterating the extra-embryonic coelom. (Figs. 16,17) That is, the amnionic cavity increases in size to the point that it occupies all of the available space inside the chorionic vesicle. As this occurs, and as the junction of amnion with the embryo is carried on to the ventral wall of the embryo, a tubular sheath of the amnion is formed. This and the structures ensheathed constitute the *umbilical cord*. Within the amnion covering the latter are the following:

1. Remnants of extra-embryonic coelom.

2. Extra-embryonic mesoderm of body stalk, here specialized as *Wharton's jelly*.

34

3. Yolk sac and the vessels which pass to and from it.

4. Allantoic diverticulum and its vessels. These vessels continue into the body stalk and, via that structure, affect connections with the chorionic vessels, ultimately becoming umbilical vessels.

E. *Yolk sac*–This saccular appendage develops on the ventral aspect of the germinal disc and has a wall of endoderm to which is later added a layer of extra-embryonic mesoderm.

1. *Primary* yolk sac–This structure is formed when the endoderm from the embryonic disc grows down on the inner surface of the trophoblast, thus forming a sac which then separates itself from the trophoblast by the development of the extra-embryonic coelom. Simultaneously the trophoblast gives rise to the extra-embryonic mesoderm which cloaks the endoderm and forms thereby the splanchnopleura or wall of the yolk sac. (Figs. 7,8)

2. *Secondary* yolk sac–During subsequent development the terminal end of the primary yolk sac becomes pinched off. The remaining portion is thereafter known as the definitive or secondary yolk sac. The roof of the yolk sac becomes folded into the developing embryo and the connection of that portion with the extra-embryonic portion becomes reduced to a narrowed *yolk stalk*. (Figs. 16,17)

3. *Function* and *fate*–As noted above the roof of the yolk sac gives rise to the gut. The yolk stalk and terminal portion of the sac are trapped within the umbilical cord and are obliterated to a greater or lesser degree. The splanchnopleura, in early stages, plays a part in the formation of blood as will be noted elsewhere in this book.

F. *Allantoic diverticulum*–This is a tubular evagination extending from the hindgut into the body stalk.

1. *Origin*–It originates as an endodermal evagination from the ventral aspect of the hindgut which extends into and is covered by the mesoderm of the body stalk. (Figs. 11,12,16)

2. *Function* and *fate*–The allantois remains relatively tiny and its functional significance is in its accompanying vessels (allantoic, then umbilical), which are utilized as the connection with the chorionic or placental circulation. The intra-embryonic portion of the allantois is continuous with the cord-like *urachus*. That portion of the allantois in the body stalk becomes incorporated into the umbilical cord where it usually undergoes obliteration.

5

Neural Tube and Somite Formation (Neurula, Somite Embryo)

I.   Review of the Presomite Embryo

Before proceeding with a consideration of the continued development of the embryo, a recapitulation of events leading up to neural tube and somite formation is in order.

A. Seven to thirteen days postovulation–At this time the conceptus is a blastocyst consisting of an outer layer of cells or trophoblast and the inner cell mass. The blastocyst has begun and in the following four days completes its implantation. During this time the embryonic disc has become bilaminar and consists of a layer of formative (ectodermal) cells and a layer of endoderm. Formation of the extra-embryonic mesoderm from the trophoblast converts that structure into the chorion, the blastocyst thereby becoming the chorionic vesicle. The amniotic cavity and yolk sac have also made their appearance. (Figs. 7,8)

B. Fourteen to twenty days postovulation–At the beginning of this period some of the formative cells of the bilaminar embryonic disc form a primitive streak. This gives rise to the intra-embryonic mesoderm which converts the disc into a trilaminar structure and, with the notochord which appears in this period, forms an axis for the elongating embryo. The notochord gains the interval between ectoderm and endoderm and the embryonic disc becomes oval, then somewhat constricted in the middle, i.e. shaped somewhat like an hour-glass. The disc bulges into the amniotic cavity along the midline and head and tail folds appear. (Figs. 9,10,11,12)

C. Twenty days postovulation–The embryo has the configuration noted immediately above. The dorsal surface shows indications of a midline groove. The chorionic vesicle is well established with definitive chorionic villi and a rudimentary cardiovascular system is just coming into being.

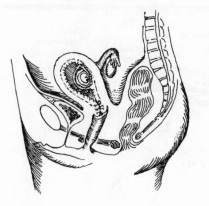

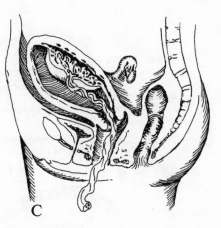

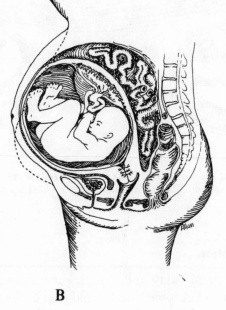

FIGURE **20.** The female pelvis in pregnancy.
A. Early pregnancy (during second month).
B. Pregnancy of full term. The dotted line indicates the configuration the abdomen takes as the fetus enters pelvis (engages) just prior to birth.
C. The uterus just prior to the delivery of the placenta.

37

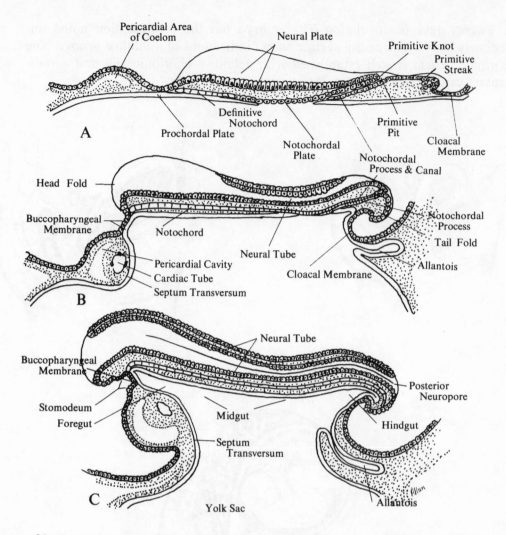

FIGURE **21.** The embryo during the fourth (and fifth) week of development (midsagittal section). A. At beginning of somite formation. B. Early somite embryo. C. Late somite embryo (early in fifth week).

II. Neural Tube Formation

At or about the 20th or 21st day of development the process of neural tube formation is undertaken and occupies the 4th and part of the 5th weeks. (Figs. 21,22)

A. Neural groove–The midline groove on the dorsal surface of the embryonic disc is called the neural groove and involves a thickened area of the ectoderm (neurectoderm) known as the *neural plate*. The groove appears just anterior to the primitive knot and, as the latter moves caudally, the groove follows. Actually, it is apparently the notochord underlying this zone which is the *organizer* or structure influential in the formation of the groove.

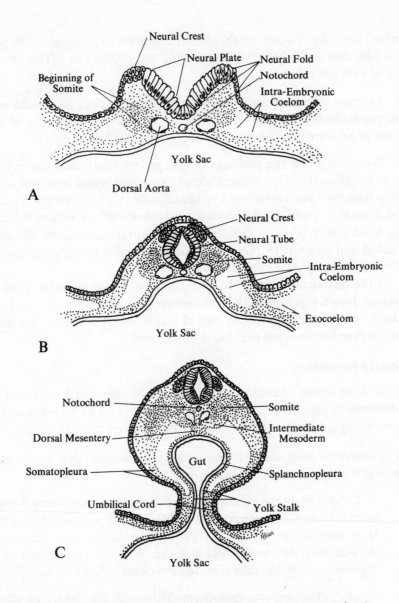

FIGURE 22. The embryo during the fourth (and fifth) week of development (cross sections). A. At beginning of somite formation (see Fig. 21A). B. Early somite embryo (see Fig. 21B). C. Late somite embryo (see Fig. 21C).

B. *Neural folds*–These are the elevations of the neural plate on either side of the neural groove. As the groove deepens the folds become accentuated and, in the middle portion of the disc, contact and fuse. Such fusion is limited to the dorsal edge (originally the lateral edge) of the fold. (Fig. 22) This converts the middle portion of the groove into the hollow:

C. *Neural tube*–The walls of the tube are formed by the neural plate material (neurectoderm) which is continuous with that of the neural folds at either

39

end of the tube. Fusion of the dorsal edges of the neural folds proceeds both cranially and caudally, thus lengthening the neural tube. The open ends of the neural tube are referred to as the:

D. *Anterior* and *posterior neuropores*—These openings are found on the cranial and caudal ends of the tube respectively. They are ultimately closed when the ends of the groove are reached by the process of neural fold fusion.

E. *Neural crest*—At the junction of the neural folds with the ectoderm proper on either side, strips of neurectoderm are noted which are also carried beneath the ectoderm when closure of the neural tube is accomplished. In the latter condition they are seen on the dorsolateral aspect of the neural tube. At first they are solid cords of cells paralleling the neural tube; they are ultimately segmented and give rise to the spinal ganglia as well as contributing to other portions of the peripheral nervous system.

As the neural tube is formed, the ectoderm lateral to either edge of the neural folds is drawn together in the midline over, or dorsal to, the newly formed tube. The latter becomes, therefore, buried and is found dorsal to the notochord. The neural tube becomes the brain and spinal cord.

III. Somite Formation

In addition to the establishment of the neural tube, the fourth and fifth week of development are characterized by the differentiation of the intra-embryonic mesoderm along either side of the notochord and neural tube. (Fig. 22)

A. Embryonic mesoderm—It should be remembered that at 20 days the intra-embryonic mesoderm is divided into:

1. Lateral plate mesoderm—This is a sheet of mesoderm forming (with related ectoderm and endoderm) the peripheral portion of the embryonic disc. It is continuous at the margin of the latter with the extra-embryonic mesoderm of the amnion and yolk sac. With the appearance of the intra-embryonic coelom, the lateral plate mesoderm is divided into:

    a. somatopleuric mesoderm—This, with the overlying ectoderm, forms the body wall or somatopleure. This mesoderm contributes to the connective, muscular, and supportive elements of the wall.

    b. splanchnopleuric mesoderm—This tissue and the endoderm which it eventually envelops form the splanchnopleure or wall of the gut and the organs derived from its diverticulae. This mesoderm gives rise to the serosa, smooth muscle, and connective tissue elements of the gut wall.

2. Intermediate mesoderm—This mesoderm lies at the medial extremity of the coelom and marks, therefore, the point of fusion of somatopleuric and splanchnopleuric mesoderm. It ultimately contributes to the formation of the gonad, kidney, and adrenal cortex.

40

3. Paraxial mesoderm–These are bilaterally placed, somewhat thickened columns of mesoderm adjacent to the notochord and, later, to the neural tube. The column is divided into a series of blocks or segments which are representative of the *metamerism* of lower vertebrates.

a. segmentation–The division of the columns of paraxial mesoderm begins at 20 days postovulation and continues to the 35th to 40th day. Most of the segmentation is complete by 30 days when 28 or 30 of the metameric blocks are laid down. These blocks or segments of mesoderm are known as:

b. somites–In all, 43 to 44 pairs of somites are formed, flanking the notochord and neural tube. They give origin to most of the axial skeleton and its associated musculature as well as the dermis of the skin. Their fate will be considered in detail elsewhere.

B. Age determination in the somite period–In estimating the age of somite embryos the following approximation can be made. The first somite appears at 20 days. Three additional somites are formed each day thereafter. Hence, at 30 days (10 days later) the embryo has 30 somites. In the subsequent week or ten days the process of somite formation becomes drawn out. The number of somites and the difficulty of distinguishing the terminal ones make the somite count less reliable as a criterion for age determination.

C. Appearance of, or changes in, other structures (systems) coincident with somite formation–This period in development is characterized by the establishment and, in some cases, the initiation of activity of most of the organ systems of the embryo. They are listed briefly below in order to acquaint the reader with the significance of this period.

1. Cardiovascular system–The endothelial tubes of the presomite embryo fuse and form a primitive circulatory system. Specialization of a portion of this system of tubes leads to the formation of the primitive heart which is functional shortly after the initiation of somite formation (at about 7 somites). It is well established at the end of the somite period. (Figs. 21,22)

2. Alimentary and respiratory systems–The primitive gut and the indication of its division into fore-, mid-, and hindgut is present at the beginning of somite formation. Completion of the division and specialization of the three segments occurs during this period, including the organs appearing as diverticulae of the latter. The primordium of the respiratory tree makes its appearance at about nine somites. (Figs. 21,22)

3. Genital and urinary systems–These systems lag behind the more precocious cardiovascular and alimentary systems. However, the pronephros appears and undergoes degeneration during the latter half of somite formation, and the other primordia, i.e. gonads, mesonephric and metanephric kidneys, appear in the late somite period.

41

4. Central nervous system—As noted above, somite and neural tube formation are simultaneously occurring processes. In addition, however, the differentiation and segmentation of the cranial portion of the tube into the primitive brain vesicle occurs during this period. (Figs. 21,22)

5. Organs of special senses—The primordia of the eye and internal ear (optic vesicle and otic placode respectively) appear early in this period and undergo simple differentiation toward the end of the period. The development of the olfactory placode lags somewhat behind and does not appear until the latter half of the period.

6. Muscular, skeletal, and integumentary systems—Since the tissues which comprise these systems are derived from the somites, the development of the systems and the differentiation of their tissues are dependent upon the formation of those somites. Obviously, therefore, derivatives of these systems appear in the more cranial regions first, an expression of the craniocaudal gradient of development. At any rate, in the latter half of the somite period representative masses destined to be muscle or bone have made their appearance. The dermatome of the integument also appears in late somite stages.

6

Review, External Body Form, Growth of Embryo and Fetus

I. Review

Although a review of the presomite embryo and the major features of its development prefaced the last chapter, it seems necessary to review this development again before proceeding to the consideration of individual organ systems.

A. Development during first week–During this period the free-living conceptus passes down the tubes and into the uterus. (Figs. 5,6)

1. Cleavage of the zygote–This is initiated by the entrance of the sperm into the ovum and is effective in reducing the ovum to cells of workable units or blastomeres.

2. Morula–The conceptus at four days post-fertilization is a solid cluster of the blastomeres. It enters the uterine cavity at this time.

3. Blastocyst–The appearance of a cavity within the morula converts it into a blastocyst. Formation of the latter and separation of its blastomeres into an outer layer of trophoblast and an inner cell mass, occupies the final portion of the first week of development.

Actually, implantation is initiated on the final day of the first week post-fertilization. For practical purposes we shall include the process of implantation as, in part, characteristic of the second week.

B. Development during the second week (Figs. 7,8)–As noted above, implantation is initiated on the seventh day. It is completed by the eleventh day and changes associated with it are reflected especially in the:

1. Modifications of the trophoblast–Actually, this structure acts as a nutritive membrane prior to implantation proper. Dissolved nutritive substances from the uterine fluids pass through the trophoblast and are utilized by the blastomeres.

43

a. syncytiotrophoblast–Upon contact with the uterine endometrium, the trophoblast of the blastocyst undergoes profound changes, resulting in the formation of an outer layer of syncytium in which cell boundaries are lost.

b. cytotrophoblast–The inner layer of the trophoblast retains its cellular nature but becomes attenuated as development proceeds.

c. chorion–This membrane is formed as implantation is completed by the appearance of the extra-embryonic mesoderm on the inner surface of the cytotrophoblast, its parent tissue. Both layers of trophoblast and the associated mesoderm constitute this membrane. Toward the end of the second week of development the chorion demonstrates the presence of chorionic villi, but their definitive form is not achieved until the third week.

2. Changes related to the inner cell mass–At the beginning of implantation the inner cell mass is separated, except at its margins, from the overlying trophoblast by a narrow cleft, the:

a. amniotic cavity–During the second week this cavity enlarges and becomes lined with the amnionic ectoderm which is derived from the trophoblast. The amnionic ectoderm gains a layer of extra-embryonic mesoderm to form the amnion.

b. embryonic plate or disc–In the same period the blastomeres of the inner cell mass, now comprising the embryonic plate or disc, have given rise to delicate endodermal cells on the surface of the disc adjacent to the blastocyst cavity. The disc becomes bilaminar, having a layer of formative cells (ectoderm) and a layer of endodermal cells. The latter encompasses the inside of the blastocyst cavity, thus forming the:

c. yolk sac–An interval, the extra-embryonic coelom, appears and expands between yolk sac and trophoblast, reducing thereby the relative size of the yolk sac. Extra-embryonic mesoderm surrounds the yolk sac to the margin of the germ disc.

C. Development during the third week–Major changes in both the chorionic vesicle and the germ disc occur during this period. (Figs. 9,10,11,18)

1. Modifications of the chorion–Early in the third week rudimentary projections of the syncytiotrophoblast extend into the maternal tissues and constitute primary chorionic villi. As the week progresses these villi become invaded by cytotrophoblast and mesoderm. Simple endothelial tubes appear in the mesoderm and anastomose to form, at the end of the week, a simple chorionic circulation, thereby rendering the villi functional or definitive. At this stage of development the chorionic villi are uniformly distributed over the entire surface of the chorionic vesicle.

2. Changes in the embryonic disc–Conversion of the bilaminar disc into one having the three germ layers is initiated and completed in this week. The intra-embryonic mesoderm is laid down by the primitive streak and gains the interval between endoderm and ectoderm. This process is associated with the elongation of the embryonic disc and the establishment of the central axis of the embryo.

D. Development during the fourth and fifth weeks (Figs. 21,22)–Changes of profound nature occur at this time. Formation of the notochord occurs, followed by formation of the neural tube and, indeed, the anlagen of all organ systems. One system, the precocious cardiovascular, becomes functional at this time. A review of the terminal portion of Chapter 5 will permit additional information on this period.

II. External Body Form

A. Presomite embryo–As has been noted previously, the embryo in early stages is a simple rounded disc which, as the primitive streak and other axial structures are formed, becomes an elongated plate or shield during the third week. At the end of this period and at the beginning of somite formation its outline is somewhat pear-shaped.

B. Somite embryo–The flattened, pear-shaped disc becomes converted into the tubular embryo with expanded cranial and, to a lesser degree, caudal ends. Although somite formation and the changes in shape mentioned above carry into the second month of development, certain structures and external features are established at this time.

1. Somites–The formation of the intra-embryonic mesoderm, its aggregation as a paraxial mass, and the subsequent segmentation of the latter into somites have been described. During their formation, the somites are easily seen beneath the delicate overlying ectoderm. Indeed, the somites are quite obvious until their differentiation, growth, and migration make them less discrete.

2. Neural groove, folds, and tube–The dorsal surface of the somite embryo is marked first by the neural groove, flanked by the neural folds, and later by the bulging neural tube after fusion of the folds is completed. The cranial end of the neural tube is markedly expanded and the anterior and posterior neuropores can be identified until their closure, which occurs in the middle of somite formation. The vesicles of the brain can be identified through the overlying ectoderm at the same time, and with the increase in the flexure of the head fold the cranial portion of the neural tube becomes similarly flexed. (Fig. 23)

45

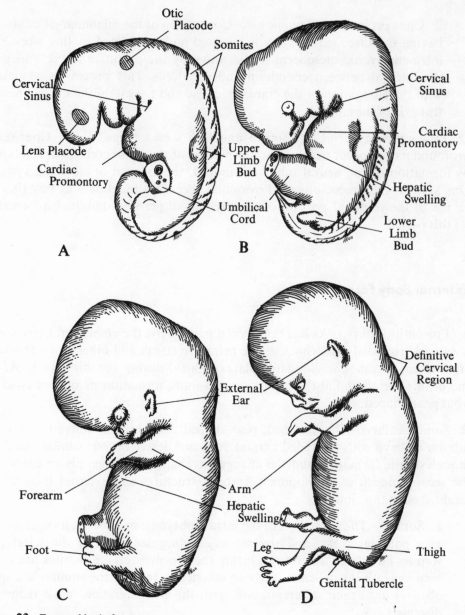

FIGURE 23. External body form.
A. Embryo at 30 days. B. Embryo at 37 days. C. Embryo at 47 days. D. Embryo at 60 days.
(after Hamilton, Boyd, and Mossman)

3. Head fold and associated branchial structures–As will be studied in detail later, the head fold of the embryo enlarges and rides forward over the *buccopharyngeal membrane* (prochordal plate and ectoderm) and the *pericardial swelling*. (Figs. 23,24)

a. *stomodeum*–This is a depressed area coinciding with the external (amniotic) surface of the buccopharyngeal membrane. It is bounded by

46

the head fold and the first branchial arch. It is seen, at this stage, as a pit in the midline under the head fold.

b. *maxillary process*-This process bounds the lateral aspect of the stomodeum.

c. *mandibular arch*-This arch, the first branchial, bounds the inferior or ventral aspect of the stomodeum and separates it from the pericardial swelling.

d. other branchial or visceral arches-These are seen as slight elevations or ridges with intervening clefts which constitute the lateral wall of the foregut.

e. sense organ primordia-Optic and otic vesicles are established during this period. The olfactory primordium is represented by the olfactory pit on the head fold.

4. *Pericardial swelling*-Originally anterior to the prochordal plate, the pericardial swelling (formed by the subjacent cardiac primordium) is carried caudally and ventrally by the overgrowth of the head fold. It forms a well-defined prominence just ventrocaudad to the mandibular arch and on the anterior aspect of the ventral body wall.

5. *Ventral body wall*-The communication of the gut with the yolk sac and the intra- with the extra-embryonic coelom maintains a wide gap in the ventral body wall. Toward the end of the period, however, the size of the communication is reduced, the umbilical cord formed, and the ventral wall established.

6. *Limb buds*-The first appearance of the limb buds as simple swellings is at the beginning of the fifth week of development. The anterior limb buds appear slightly earlier than the posterior limb buds.

7. *Tail*-The tail is prominent toward the end of this period but soon undergoes an actual and relative decrease in size.

C. Embryo during the second month of development-During this period the embryo assumes many of the external features that mark it as human.

1. Somites-The somites become increasingly difficult to identify. They are all formed by the sixth week.

2. Neural tube and derivatives-The expansion of the primitive brain vesicles can be followed through the first half of the second month.

3. Head fold and associated structures-The most significant changes involve the formation of the face by the modifications of the branchial (especially mandibular) arches and the maxillary and *frontonasal* processes. (Fig. 24)

47

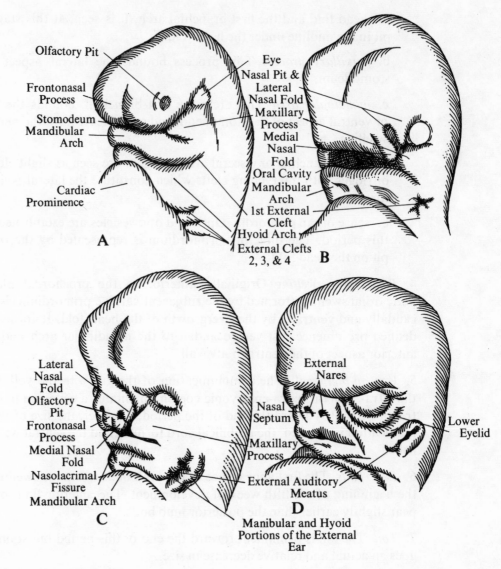

Olfactory Pit

Frontonasal Process

Stomodeum
Mandibular Arch

Cardiac Prominence

Eye
Nasal Pit & Lateral Nasal Fold
Maxillary Process
Medial Nasal Fold
Oral Cavity
Mandibular Arch
1st External Cleft
Hyoid Arch
External Clefts 2, 3, & 4

A

B

Lateral Nasal Fold
Olfactory Pit
Frontonasal Process
Medial Nasal Fold
Nasolacrimal Fissure
Mandibular Arch

External Nares

Nasal Septum

Maxillary Process

External Auditory Meatus

Lower Eyelid

Manibular and Hyoid Portions of the External Ear

C

D

FIGURE 24. Development of the face.
A. Embryo at 34 days. B. Embryo at 37 days. C. Embryo at 40 days. D. Embryo at 48 days.

a. stomodeum–This area deepens and forms the common naso-oral cavity.

b. maxillary process–Fusion of the maxillary process with the *lateral*, then *medial, nasal folds* below the developing eye and above stomodeum is completed at the beginning of the seventh week.

c. mandibular process (arch)–This structure forms the lower jaw and, due to the sharp flexure of the head on the trunk, is buried in the interval between face and pericardial swelling.

48

d. hyoid and other branchial arches–To be considered with the neck (below).

e. sense organ primordia–The eye is a prominent external feature throughout the period. The otic vesicle can be seen in the first half of the month. Thereafter it is obscured by the development of the external ear which at this time is noted as the dorsal extremity of the first *branchial cleft* or *groove* and adjacent portions of the mandibular and hyoid arches which exhibit several small hillocks or elevations. The olfactory primordium (olfactory placode) has sunk from the surface, creating the *nasal pit* flanked by the medial and lateral nasal folds whose fusion with the maxillary process has been referred to above.

4. Neck–The lower four branchial arches form a depression between head and trunk known as the cervical sinus. The hyoid or second branchial arch grows caudally, obliterating the sinus during the latter half of the second month. Modification of the cervical flexures and a lengthening of the area lead to the appearance of the neck.

5. Pericardial swelling and ventral body wall–In the middle of the second month the pericardial swelling merges with the hepatic swelling, and the upper abdomen appears somewhat globose. Reduction of the circumference of the umbilical attachment is noted and results in the better definition of the ventral body wall. At the caudal end of the latter, the external genital primordia make their appearance toward the end of this period.

6. Limbs–These are seen in the first week of this period as simple swellings. A week later the arm, forearm, wrist, and hand are outlined but the lower extremity remains more rudimentary. At the end of the period the digits on the hand are apparent and the thigh, leg, and foot also, with rays on the last indicating the position of the digits. By the end of this period both upper and lower limbs are well defined.

III. **Growth of Embryo–**

Correlation of Age, Size, Number of Somites, etc.–It should be noted here that the measurements used below only approximate reality. Additional material and study is necessary to make more accurate our knowledge in this area.

A. Zygote–The fertilized egg or zygote is about 140 micra (.14 mm.) in diameter.

B. Blastocyst

1. Pre-implantation–At seven days the diameter of the blastocyst is about 0.2 mm. The inner cell mass or embryonic disc is about 0.1 mm. in diameter.

2. Post-implantation–At eleven days the diameter of the blastocyst (now the chorionic vesicle) is 0.8 mm. and the embryonic disc is about 0.15 mm. long.

C. Late presomite embryo (18 days)–The chorionic vesicle now measures 8 mm. in diameter and the embryonic disc 1.3 mm. long.

D. Somite embryo–The measurements noted here are from the crown of the head to the rump of the embryo. During the somite period about three somites are added each day. However, the rate lags toward the end of somite formation.

    1. One somite embryo (20-21 days)–The chorionic vesicle now measures 10 mm. in diameter (and continues to grow about 10 mm. per week until the second month) and the embryo is about 1.5 mm. long.

    2. Ten somite embryo (about 23 days)–The embryo is about 1.8 mm. long.

    3. Twenty somite embryo (about 26 days)–The embryo is about 3.0 mm. long.

    4. Thirty somite embryo (about 30-31 days)–The embryo is about 4.5 mm. long.

E. Embryos of the second month–At 32 days the embryo is five mm. long. To the end of the second month the rate of growth is about one mm. per day. Hence, at 56 days the embryo is about 30 mm. long. At the end of this period the embryo weighs one gram.

F. Fetal growth from the third month to term–The rate of growth in length is about one and one-half mm. per day, although growth slacks off somewhat near term. Increase in weight cannot be reduced to as simple a formula as that given for length. However, the increase during the third month is 14-fold. During subsequent months this rate is decreased considerably. Nevertheless, at term the fetus usually weighs about 3300 grams or 3300 times as much as it did at the end of the second month.

It should be noted that termination of pregnancy occurs approximately 280 days from the beginning of the last menstrual period. Factors which influence the termination of pregnancy are only partially known and may be a combination of mechanical and hormonal effects.

7

Cardiovascular System: Development of the Heart

I. Introduction

During the first three weeks of development the conceptus is nourished by the diffusion of nutrients obtained from the uterine lumen and, after implantation, the maternal blood lake. However, the rapid growth of the trophoblast and chorionic vesicle limits the effectiveness of nutrition by this means. The precocious development of the circulation of the embryo, including the extra-embryonic portion, i.e. that portion within the chorion and body stalk, provides the means by which the developing embryo can be nourished. It should be remembered that the simple circulatory system established so early must undergo repeated modifications, while remaining functional, in order to adapt to the ever-changing needs of the developing embryo.

II. Presomite Embryo

A. Nourishment–As noted above, the conceptus prior to implantation receives nutrients by simple diffusion from the secretions of the uterine glands. These secretions are of a mucous nature and are rich in glycogen. After implantation has taken place and until the embryonic circulatory system is established, nutrition is accomplished by utilization of diffusible substances from the embryotrophe within the maternal blood lake. The embryotrophe consists of the digested cells of the uterine endometrium, extravasated blood, and the secretions of the uterine glands involved in the implantation process. As more and more of the uterine tissues are involved by the invasive chorionic vesicle, a greater and greater number of endometrial vessels are eroded and the chief component of the embryotrophe becomes maternal blood. The trophoblast is converted into the chorion which then forms the chorionic villi bathed by the maternal blood within the (now) intervillous spaces.

51

B. Changes leading to the formation of the embryonic cardiovascular system—

1. Endothelium—The simple one cell thick tubes which are the precursor of the lining of the cardiovascular system and are comparable to the capillaries of that system arise *in situ* from the mesoderm (perhaps also yolk sac endoderm) in various areas of the conceptus. They appear as isolated cords of cells which later form lumina and link together, resulting in simple vascular networks. This tissue is called the angioblast and arises almost simultaneously during the middle of the third week of development in the following areas:

a. splanchnopleuric mesoderm—Located in the yolk sac, these tubes become the vitelline system of vessels.

b. body stalk and chorion—These tubes become the umbilical system of vessels which form the vascular network of the placenta. In the body stalk they develop closely associated with the allantois.

c. embryo proper—The simple vascular system of the embryo lags slightly behind the above-mentioned areas. Nevertheless, a double system of vessels is established, consisting of the cardinal veins and the aorta, its arches and branches. The veins and aorta are united by the simple vessels of the cardiogenic area located just anterior to the prochordal plate.

2. Blood formation—In the wall of the yolk sac and in the body stalk the angioblastic tissue forms blood islands which are converted into vessels and blood. This is achieved as the central cells of a cluster or cord become trapped within the primitive vessels and form thereby the cells of the blood. The plasma apparently arises from the cells of the blood island.

III. Somite Embryo

Coincident with the formation of the first somites a functional, although simple, circulatory system is established which utilizes the simple vascular networks formed in the presomite embryo. (Figs. 21,22,25) These networks can be divided into:

A. Intra-embryonic vascular system

1. Cardiogenic vessels—The originally paired, simple endothelial tubes of the cardiogenic mesoderm which are found just anterior to the prochordal plate, fuse and gain a tunic of mesoderm which soon acquires a rhythmic contractility. The *cardiac tube* thus formed is linked with the aorta and the venous system which have both intra- and extra-embryonic areas of distribution.

52

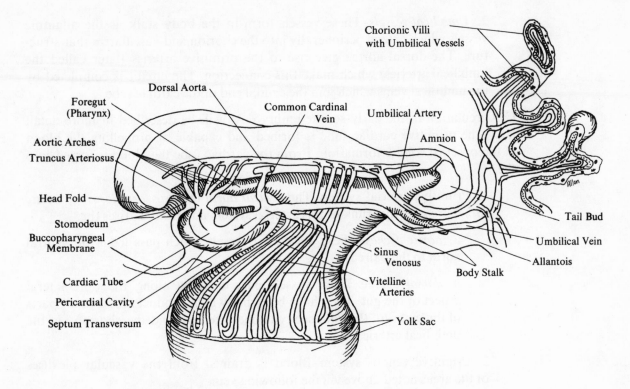

The figure includes the following labels:

Chorionic Villi with Umbilical Vessels
Dorsal Aorta
Foregut (Pharynx)
Common Cardinal Vein
Umbilical Artery
Aortic Arches
Truncus Arteriosus
Amnion
Head Fold
Stomodeum
Buccopharyngeal Membrane
Tail Bud
Cardiac Tube
Umbilical Vein
Pericardial Cavity
Sinus Venosus
Allantois
Body Stalk
Septum Transversum
Vitelline Arteries
Yolk Sac

FIGURE 25. Primitive circulatory system.

2. *Aortae*–These vessels are part of the arterial side of circulation and consist, in early stages, of the paired *dorsal aortae* which are connected to one end of the cardiac tube. These vessels pass caudally parallel and ventral to the notochord. Subsequent branching of these vessels will be noted in the next chapter.

3. *Cardinal veins*–These vessels drain the body wall and, with the intra-embryonic portion of the vitelline and umbilical veins, join the caudal end of the cardiac tube.

4. The terminal portions of umbilical and vitelline vessels–These are continuous with the caudal end of the cardiac tube.

B. Extra-embryonic vascular system

1. *Vitelline vessels*–These paired vessels form from the vascular plexus in the wall of the yolk sac and later, therefore, are to be found in the wall of the gut. Branches from the dorsal aortae extend to the roof of the yolk sac, thus linking the vessels developed *in situ* with the arterial system. Vitelline veins in the roof of the yolk sac anastomose with the caudal end of the cardiac tube, as noted above, to complete the circuit.

53

2. *Umbilical vessels*-These vessels form in the body stalk as the allantoic vessels which extend peripherally into the chorion and vascularize that structure. The dorsal aortae give rise to the primitive arteries (later called the umbilical arteries) which make this connection. The circuit is completed by the umbilical veins which join the caudal end of the cardiac tube.

C. Circulation in the early somite embryo-As will be described in more detail later, the primitive cardiac tube is formed and capable of propelling the blood at the onset of somite formation. From the cardiac tube the blood is forced into the:

1. Primitive arterial system-The *ventral aorta* (*truncus arteriosus* or *aortic sac*) represents the trunk of this arterial system and from it arises the:

   a. *aortic arches*-These are paired vessels which pass from the ventral aorta to the paired:

   b. *dorsal aortae*-These vessels pass caudally along the dorsolateral aspect of the gut. They have branches which conduct blood to all parts of the embryo, the yolk sac (vitelline arteries), and the chorion via the umbilical arteries.

2. Primitive venous system-Blood is drained from the vascular plexuses of the areas noted above via the following veins:

   a. *umbilical veins*-The blood from the capillary plexuses of the chorionic villi is conveyed by the umbilical veins through the body stalk and into the caudal portion of the cardiac tube. Just prior to entering the heart it is mixed with blood from the:

   b. vitelline veins-Blood from vessels in the roof and wall of the yolk sac is conveyed toward the heart where it mingles with blood from the umbilical veins in a common sinus (*sinus venosus*).

   c. *common cardinal veins*-Blood which reaches the vascular plexuses of the embryo proper is drained by the cardinal system of veins which, via the paired common cardinal veins, empties into the common sinus.

IV. Development of the Heart

A. Cardiogenic area-The splanchnopleuric mesoderm anterior to the prochordal plate and ventral to the pericardial portion of the coelom gives rise to two simple endothelial tubes which fuse to form the unpaired midline cardiac primordium. From mesodermal cells adjacent to the endothelial tube a mantle called the epimyocardium is differentiated which develops an intrinsic ability to contract. With formation of the head fold, this area is rotated through 180 degrees and comes to lie ventral to the pharyngeal portion of the foregut. The cardiac primordium is, at this point, suspended from the now dorsal wall of the pericardial cavity. The caudal end of the cardiac tube is the venous end, whereas the cephalic end is the arterial end of the primordium.

B. Cardiac tube–The tube is fixed at its cephalic (arterial) and caudal (venous) extremities as it passes from the pericardial cavity. As development proceeds the tube elongates and is bent into a U-shaped loop with the cephalic extremity anterior or ventral to the caudal extremity. The tube is divided into four segments, which will be considered in detail below (Fig. 26):

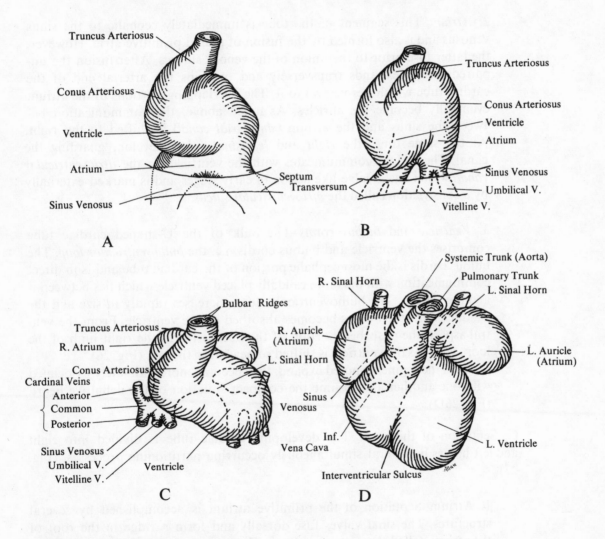

FIGURE 26. Development of the heart (external view).
A. From a 12 somite embryo (24 days). B. From a 20–22 somite embryo (26–27 days).
C. From a 30 somite embryo (30 days). D. From a 14 mm. embryo (40–41 days).

55

1. *Sinus venosus*–Located at the caudal end of the tube this segment is originally paired as the unfused ends of the cardiac tubes and located in the substance of the transverse septum (derived from splanchnopleuric mesoderm). Due to the expansion of the pericardial cavity the primitive sinuses come to lie within the cavity and fusion of the paired sinuses takes place except for the caudalmost extremities which are retained as the *right* and *left sinal horns*. With continued development and due to the shifting of the bulk of the venous blood to the right sinal horn, the left sinal horn is reduced in size. The body of the sinus and its communication with the atrium are also shifted to the right.

2. *Atrium*–This segment of the tube is immediately cephalic to the sinus venosus and is also formed by the fusion of paired primitive atria. However, the latter fuse prior to the union of the venous sinuses. After fusion the unpaired atrium expands transversely and overlaps the arterial end of the cardiac tube which lies ventral to it. The overlapping portions of the atrium eventually become the auricles. As noted above, the communication between the sinus and the atrium (*sino-atrial canal*) is shifted to the right. At the same time, the *right* and *left sinal valves* develop, guarding the canal. The atrium communicates with the ventricle via the *atrioventricular canal*, which has a valve-like action in early stages and is marked externally by a constriction called the *atrioventricular sulcus*.

3. *Ventricle* and *bulbus cordis*–The bulk of the U-shaped cardiac tube comprises the ventricle and bulbus cordis, i.e. the *bulboventricular loop*. The bulbus cordis is the most cephalic portion of the cardiac tube and is in direct communication with the more caudally placed ventricle which lies between it and the atrium. The bulboventricular loop increases rapidly in size and the caudal end of the bulbus becomes absorbed by the ventricle. From the ventral aspect, the absorbed portion of the bulbus forms the right limb of the loop, whereas the ventricle is shifted somewhat to the left. (Fig. 26)

As all the segments noted expand, they become more intimately associated with one another and assume the compact situation of the definitive heart. (Fig. 26D)

C. Septation of the heart–The developing cardiac tube is divided into right and left halves by several simultaneously occurring partitioning processes. (Fig. 27)

1. Atrium–Septation of the primitive atrium is accomplished by several structures. The sinal valves fuse dorsally and form a ridge in the roof of the atrium called the *septum spurium*. The latter is not used in the septation process, but just to the left of the septum spurium a ridge appears which becomes the:

56

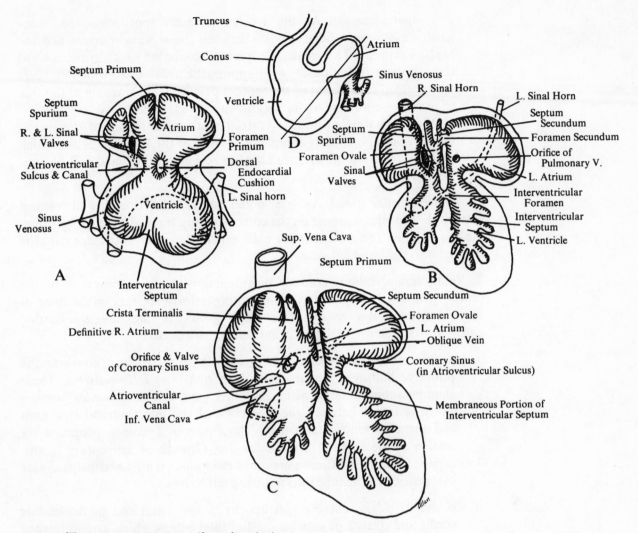

FIGURE **27.** Septation of the heart (frontal section).
A. From a 5 mm. embryo (32 days). B. From a 20 mm. embryo (47 days).
C. From a 40 mm. embryo (about 2 1/2 months). D. Sagittal section showing plane of section of A.

a. *septum primum*–This ridge is sickle-shaped and bounds the *foramen primum*. As the septum primum increases in size the foramen primum undergoes a corresponding decrease in diameter; ultimately, the septum fuses with the:

b. *dorsal and ventral endocardial cushions*–These are ridges in the corresponding sides of the atrioventricular canal. Fusion of the endocardial cushions with each other and the septum primum obliterates the foramen primum. Prior to the obliteration, however, the cephalic portion of the septum primum breaks down, forming a second interatrial communication called the *foramen secundum*.

57

c. *septum secundum*-As the septum primum approaches the endocardial cushions, a ridge appears between the septum spurium and the septum primum. This ridge is the septum secundum which grows toward the atrioventricular canal, overlapping the free edge (which borders the foramen secundum) of the septum primum. The opening at the free edge of the septum secundum is known as the *foramen ovale.*

With formation of both interatrial septa, partitioning of the primitive atrium is potentially complete. Closure of the foramen ovale, which makes separation of the atria absolute, occurs at birth and will be considered later.

2. *Atrioventricular canal*-As was noted above, the dorsal and ventral endocardial cushions appear on the corresponding sides of the atrioventricular canal. Upon their fusion with each other, the atrioventricular canal is divided into right and left sides.

3. Ventricle and bulbus cordis-Coincidental with the appearance of the septum primum, a ridge directed antero-posteriorly appears in the floor of the bulboventricular cavity. This ridge grows toward the endocardial cushions of the atrioventricular canal and constitutes the:

a. *interventricular septum*-By its growth this structure converts the primitive bulboventricular cavity into *right* and *left ventricles.* These chambers communicate with each other via the *interventricular foramen* which is found between the free edge of the interventricular septum and the atrioventricular canal. The foramen becomes progressively smaller as the septum increases in size. Growth of the septum is also carried into the proximal portion of the bulbus cordis and helps divide that portion of the tube into right and left halves.

b. *bulbar ridges*-These ridges appear at the distal end of the bulbus cordis and consist of subendocardial thickenings which extend toward the interventricular septum in a spiral manner. In so doing, they complete a 180 degree spiral, unite with each other, and fuse proximally with the interventricular septum and establish the ventricular outlets, i.e. the pulmonary trunk (from the right) and the aorta (from the left).

D. Further changes in the heart-With the completion of septation at the end of the seventh week, additional changes of the heart are less dramatic and involve modifications of the various structures mentioned above. (Fig. 27C) A final recapitulation of the primitive segments and the structures derived therefrom seems in order here.

1. Sinus venosus-The right sinal horn is absorbed into and becomes the greater part of the *definitive right atrium.* The left sinal horn and transverse portion of the primitive sinus are retained as the *oblique vein,* on the

58

dorsal wall of the *definitive left atrium*, and the *coronary sinus*, respectively. The left sinal valve contributes to the formation of the atrial septum, as noted above, and the right sinal valve is retained as the *crista terminalis* (marking junction of sinal and atrial portions of the definitive right atrium), the *intervenous tubercle* (of Lower), the *valve of the inferior vena cava*, and the *valve of the coronary sinus*.

2. Primitive atrium–The right and left halves of the primitive atrium are retained as the corresponding *auricles* of the definitive heart. The fused primitive interatrial septa (septum primum and septum secundum) are retained as the *atrial septum* with the contribution of the left sinal valve as noted above. The expansion of the atria by incorporation of the sinus venosus on the right side has been mentioned above. On the left side expansion of the atrium absorbs the bases of the *pulmonary veins*.

3. Primitive ventricle–The left ventricle and the bulk of the right ventricle of the definitive heart are derived from the primitive ventricle. The ventricular septum is retained as the muscular portion of the definitive septum.

4. Atrioventricular canal–This communication is divided into right and left canals by the dorsal and ventral endocardial cushions. The cushions also take part in the formation of the *right (tricuspid)* and *left (bicuspid) atrioventricular valves* which guard the right and left canals respectively. The cushions also contribute to the septum secundum and the membraneous portion of the interventricular septum.

5. Bulbus cordis–As noted previously, this segment of the primitive cardiac tube is essentially absorbed by the right ventricle where it forms the *conus arteriosus*. Its distal portion is included in the root of both the aorta and the pulmonary trunk. The bulbar ridges separate the latter vessels and also contribute to the *membraneous interventricular septum*. The ridges also aid in the formation of the semilunar valves which guard the aortic and pulmonary trunks.

6. Cardiac valves–The origin of the various cardiac valves has been considered above. It should be added, however, that the atrioventricular valves appear as subendocardial thickenings, later invaded by muscle, and ultimately thinned by an undermining process. Certain areas are avoided by the undermining process resulting in columns of tissue attached to the valve. These columns are converted into the *papillary muscles* and their connections with the valves become thinned to form the *chordae tendinae*.

8

Cardiovascular System: Arteries and Veins

I. Morphology of the Primitive Vascular System

It has been noted that blood vessels are formed by confluence of simple endothelial tubes which, in turn, form plexuses in the embryonic tissues adaptable
to the changing requirements of the tissue. Depending upon the route the blood
takes through a plexus, certain vessels will be enlarged to accommodate the
increase, whereas those from which blood is diverted remain small or
revert and disappear. The vessels which persist develop additional layers of
smooth muscle and connective tissue for additional strength and adaptability to
functional needs.

A. Cardiac tube–The origin and modification of this segment of the vascular
system have been described in detail in the previous chapter. Let it suffice here
to say that it forms an increasingly complex pump which propels blood through
the vessels of the embryo.

B. Arterial system–This system of vessels conducts blood from the heart into
the lungs (pulmonary division) or into the other tissues (systemic division) of
the body. In early stages of development these divisions are not separated. (Figs.
28,29)

1. Ventral aorta (truncus arteriosus, aortic sac)–This vessel is continuous
with the cephalic end of the cardiac tube. It serves as the main stem of the
arterial system. It lies ventral to the primitive pharynx where it gives origin
to the:

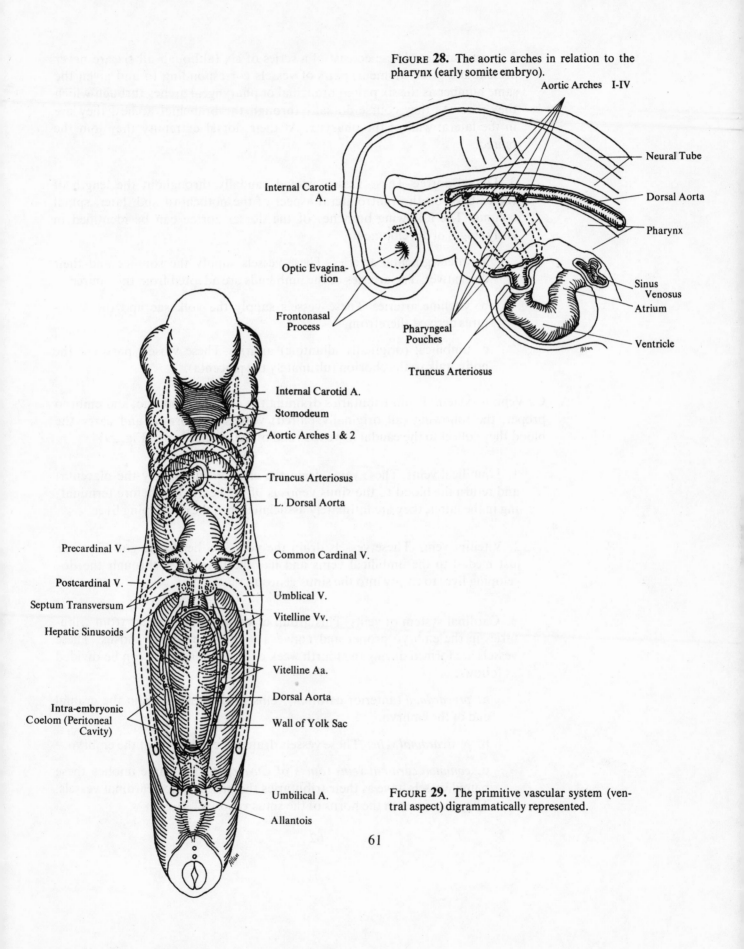

FIGURE **28.** The aortic arches in relation to the pharynx (early somite embryo).

Aortic Arches I-IV

Neural Tube

Dorsal Aorta

Pharynx

Sinus Venosus

Atrium

Ventricle

Internal Carotid A.

Optic Evagination

Frontonasal Process

Pharyngeal Pouches

Truncus Arteriosus

Internal Carotid A.
Stomodeum
Aortic Arches 1 & 2
Truncus Arteriosus
L. Dorsal Aorta

Precardinal V.

Postcardinal V.

Septum Transversum

Hepatic Sinusoids

Intra-embryonic Coelom (Peritoneal Cavity)

Common Cardinal V.

Umblical V.

Vitelline Vv.

Vitelline Aa.

Dorsal Aorta

Wall of Yolk Sac

Umbilical A.

Allantois

FIGURE **29.** The primitive vascular system (ventral aspect) digrammatically represented.

61

2. Aortic arches–These consist of a series of six (although all six are never present at a given moment) pairs of vessels corresponding to and given the same number as the six paired branchial or pharyngeal arches through which they pass. As they course dorsally through the branchial arches, they are in the lateral wall of the pharynx. At their dorsal extremity they join the paired:

3. Dorsal aortae–These vessels extend caudally throughout the length of the embryo on the ventrolateral aspect of the notochord and, later, spinal column. The following branches of the dorsal aortae can be identified in early stages of development:

a. intersegmental arteries–These vessels supply the somites and their derivatives. The arteries to the limb buds are adapted from this source.

b. vitelline arteries–These vessels supply the yolk sac and the structures derived therefrom.

c. umbilical (originally allantoic) arteries–These vessels pass via the body stalk to the chorion (ultimately the placenta).

C. Venous system–From tributaries draining the chorion, yolk sac, and embryo proper, the following (all originally paired) vessels are formed and carry the blood they collect to the caudal or venous end of the cardiac tube. (Fig. 29)

1. Umbilical veins–These veins drain the chorion (ultimately the placenta) and return the blood to the sinus venosus of the heart. Just before terminating in the latter, they are intimately associated with the developing liver.

2. Vitelline veins–These vessels drain the yolk sac, hence the gut. They lie just medial to the umbilical veins and like the latter pass through the developing liver to empty into the sinus venosus.

3. Cardinal system of veins–This group of vessels drains blood from tributaries in the embryo proper and conveys it into the sinus venosus. These vessels are formed during the fourth week of development and can be divided as follows:

a. *precardinal* (anterior cardinal) veins–These vessels drain the cranial end of the embryo.

b. *postcardinal veins*–These vessels drain the caudal end of the embryo.

c. *common cardinal veins* (*ducts of Cuvier*)–As the name implies these paired vessels have as their tributaries the pre- and postcardinal vessels. They terminate in the horns of the sinus venosus.

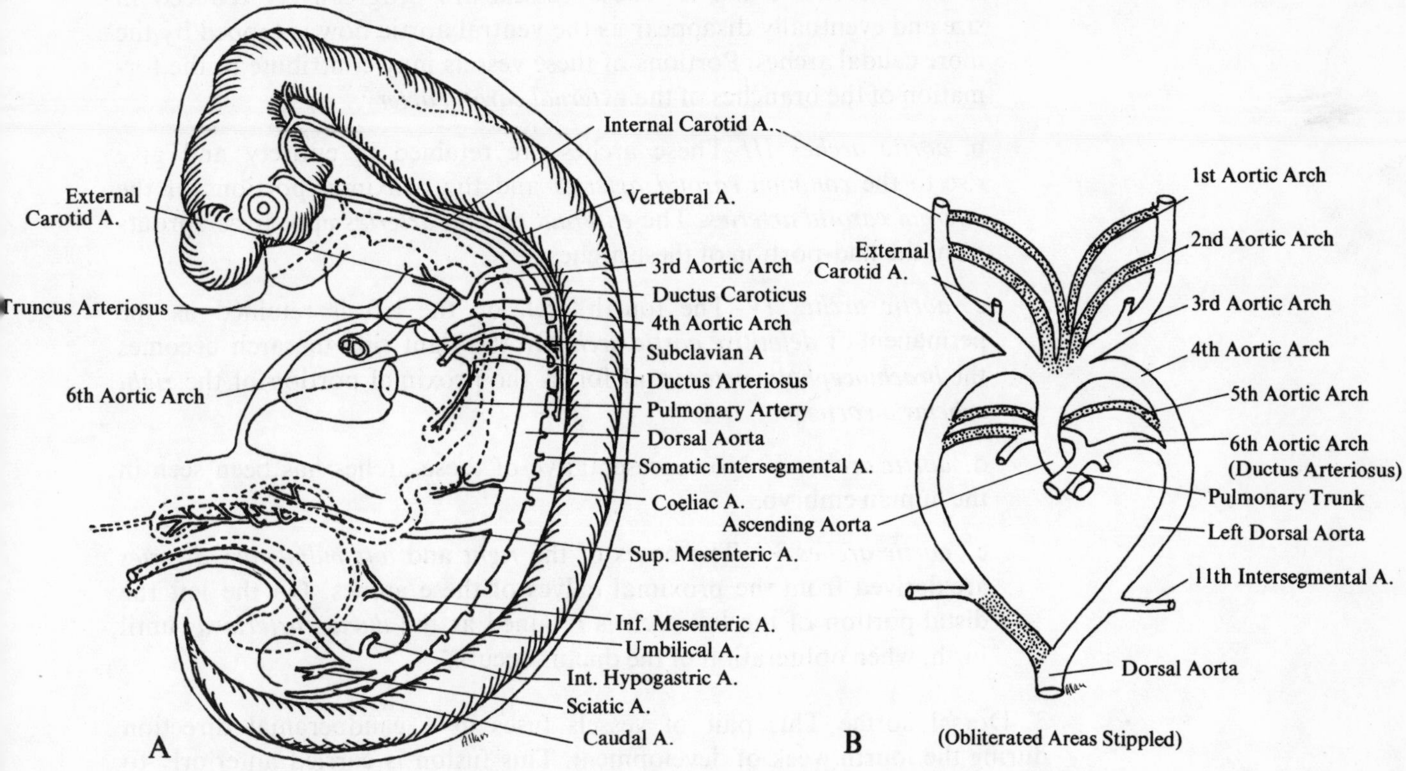

Internal Carotid A.
External
Carotid A.
Vertebral A.
3rd Aortic Arch
Truncus Arteriosus
Ductus Caroticus
4th Aortic Arch
Subclavian A
6th Aortic Arch
Ductus Arteriosus
Pulmonary Artery
Dorsal Aorta
Somatic Intersegmental A.
Coeliac A.
Sup. Mesenteric A.
Inf. Mesenteric A.
Umbilical A.
Int. Hypogastric A.
Sciatic A.
Caudal A.
A
1st Aortic Arch
External
Carotid A.
2nd Aortic Arch
3rd Aortic Arch
4th Aortic Arch
5th Aortic Arch
6th Aortic Arch
(Ductus Arteriosus)
Pulmonary Trunk
Ascending Aorta
Left Dorsal Aorta
11th Intersegmental A.
Dorsal Aorta
B
(Obliterated Areas Stippled)

FIGURE **30.** A. The arterial system in a 10 mm. embryo (about 37 days). B. Fate of the aortic arches.

II. Modification and Fate of the Primitive Vascular Pattern

In order to fulfill the needs of the developing embryo numerous changes in the primitive vascular pattern are necessitated and are indicated below: (Figs. 30,31)

A. Arterial system

1. Ventral aorta (truncus arteriosus)–The ventral aorta is divided into *pulmonary* and *systemic trunks* by the splitting action of the bulbar ridges noted in Chapter 7. Distally the pulmonary trunk comes to lie dorsal to the systemic trunk. The first five pairs of aortic arches take origin from the systemic trunk, whereas the sixth aortic arch arises from the pulmonary trunk.

2. Aortic arches–These vessels pass through the mesoderm of their respective branchial arches intimately associated with the nerves and other structures which differentiate within the branchial arches. The aortic arches appear and disappear or are modified in conformity to the cranio-caudal gradient of growth. All the arches have made their appearance by the end of the fourth week. Their modification and transformation are undertaken and completed in the subsequent two weeks. (Figs. 29,30A,B)

a. *aortic arches I and II*–These vessels are progressively reduced in size and eventually disappear as the ventral aortic flow is tapped by the more caudal arches. Portions of these vessels may contribute to the formation of the branches of the *external carotid artery*.

b. *aortic arches III*–These arches are retained in entirety and give rise to the *common carotid arteries* and the proximal portions of the *internal carotid arteries*. The *external carotid arteries* appear as sprouts from the mid-portion of these arches.

c. *aortic arches IV*–The fourth arch on the left is retained as the permanent or *definitive aortic arch*. On the right side the arch becomes the *brachiocephalic artery* and forms the proximal portion of the *right subclavian artery*.

d. *aortic arches V*–No representative of these arches has been seen in the human embryo.

e. *aortic arches VI*–The bases of the *right* and *left pulmonary arteries* are derived from the proximal halves of these arches. On the left the distal portion of the left arch is retained as the *ductus arteriosus* until birth, when obliteration of the ductus occurs.

3. Dorsal aortae–This pair of vessels fuses in a caudocranial direction during the fourth week of development. This fusion is carried anteriorly to the eleventh (seventh cervical) intersegmental artery:

a. *cephalic portion*–The dorsal aortae cranial to the entrance of the third aortic arches form the bulk of the *internal carotid arteries*.

b. *ductus caroticus*–The segment of each dorsal aorta between junctions of the third and fourth aortic arches is retained for a short while as the ductus caroticus. (Fig. 30) It is, of course, bilaterally represented.

c. *right dorsal aorta*–Between the junction of the fourth arch and the eleventh intersegmental artery on the right side the dorsal aorta is retained as the *right subclavian artery*. The short terminal portion, i.e. between the eleventh intersegmental artery and the union with the left dorsal aorta, is obliterated.

d. *left dorsal aorta*–Caudal to the juncture of the fourth arch, the left dorsal aorta and that portion derived from the fused dorsal aortae are retained as the *definitive descending aorta*.

4. *Aortic branches*–The simple series of branches from the fused dorsal aorta is made more complex with the appearance of branches to newly formed structures and organs. A consideration of the basic pattern of the definitive vascular system is here presented:

64

a. intersegmental somatic arteries–These vessels were noted above as passing to the somites and their derivatives. Each vessel divides into *dorsal* and *ventral rami.* The dorsal rami pass to, and supply, the dorsal aspect of the embryo, including the spinal cord and vertebral column. The ventral rami pass essentially to the lateral and ventral body wall. In the thoracic region the ventral rami become the *intercostal arteries.* The anastomosis of adjacent dorsal rami in the cervical region leads to the formation of the *vertebral arteries.* The latter extend cranially and join the unpaired *basilar artery* (formed *in situ*) on the ventral aspect of the brain stem. The latter vessel, in turn, gives rise to branches which, in part, form the *circle of Willis* by joining the cranial extremity of the internal carotid arteries.

b. arteries of the extremities–Certain of the intersegmental arteries opposite the limb buds become specialized as the main vessels to the developing extremity. In this regard the eleventh (seventh cervical) intersegmental arteries on each side form *subclavian arteries* (note the contribution to the right subclavian artery by aortic segments described above) which become the main vessels of the upper extremity. The vessels to the lower extremity are more complicated in their origin. Let it suffice to say that the *common iliac arteries* arise as intersegmental vessels which tap the primitive umbilical arteries on each side. From each common iliac artery two vessels are given off which pass to each lower extremity. One of these is the *sciatic artery* which forms the main vessel to the limb in early stages. It is superseded by the *femoral artery,* a direct continuation of the *external iliac artery* which arises as a bud from the common iliac vessel.

c. vitelline arteries–Originally these arteries constitute a series of paired vessels from the paired dorsal aortae to the yolk sac and, later, the gut. With fusion of the aortae there is an apparent fusion of paired vessels until, at the end of the fifth week of development, three unpaired ventral branches of the definitive aorta persist. They are, in craniocaudal sequence, the:

(1) *coeliac trunk* or *artery*–This vessel supplies structures or organs derived from the caudal end of the foregut.
(2) *superior mesenteric artery*–This vessel supplies the structures derived from the larger portion of the midgut, i.e. all of the cranial and most of the caudal limbs of the midgut.
(3) *inferior mesenteric artery*–This artery supplies structures derived from the caudal portion of the midgut and the bulk of the hindgut.

65

d. umbilical arteries–These vessels arise from the paired dorsal aortae and remain paired even after fusion, which occurs very early, of the latter vessels. As noted above, however, the umbilical arteries fuse with the adjacent intersegmental (common iliac) vessels with the result that their proximal portions obliterate and the blood they carry first passes through the common iliac arteries. A portion of the umbilical artery just distal to the juncture with the common iliac becomes converted into the *hypogastric* or *internal iliac artery* which supplies the structures derived from the caudal end of the hindgut, including the allantoic diverticulum.

e. *bilateral* or *intersegmental splanchnic arteries*–These are lateral branches of the dorsal aorta which supply structures derived from the intermediate mesoderm. Most of the vessels degenerate or coalesce with adjacent arteries so that definitively only the following are retained:

(1) *inferior phrenic artery*–This is retained as a source of blood to the adrenal gland. It also supplies the diaphragm.
(2) *adrenal* or *suprarenal arteries*–As the names imply these vessels supply the adrenal gland.
(3) *renal arteries*–These vessels supply the kidneys.
(4) *gonadal arteries*–These vessels supply the gonads. In the male they are called the *testicular arteries;* in the female, *ovarian arteries.*

B. Venous system–The vessels considered here are all tributaries of the sinus venosus. (Figs. 31,32,33,34,35)

1. Vitelline veins–These vessels drain the primitive gut and as development and differentiation of that structure occur, a transformation of the vitelline veins follows. This transformation begins during the fifth week of development. The picture is further complicated, however, by the fact that the proximal or cranial portions of the vitelline veins are included in the substance of the developing liver. Nevertheless, the following adult derivatives of the vitelline veins can be noted: (Fig. 31D)

a. proximal portion of the *inferior vena cava*–This structure is derived from the base of the right vitelline vein.

b. *hepatic veins*–As the cords of liver cells grow into the vitelline veins they break the latter into a large number of smaller, intercommunicating sinusoids which are later utilized as the hepatic veins.

c. *portal vein*–Caudal to the liver, the primitive vitelline veins embrace the gut. A number of cross anastomoses between the paired vessels occurs and eventually a single vessel, the portal vein, is derived from the complex. (Fig. 31) The main portion and tributaries of the

66

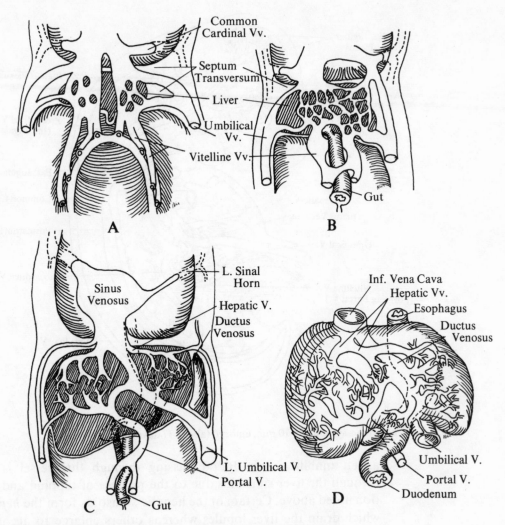

FIGURE 31. Modification of the hepatic-portal system of veins (ventral views).
A. Early (5–10) somite embryo (22–23 days). B. Mid (24–26) somite embryo (28 days).
C. Late (34–36, 5 mm.) somite embryo (32 days). D. Characteristic of late embryonic and fetal life.

portal vein, the *superior* and *inferior mesenteric veins,* are also derived
from the vitelline complex.

2. Umbilical veins–These veins drain the placenta and, like the vitelline
vessels, are intimately associated with the developing liver as they approach
the sinus venosus. Their transformation begins during the fifth and is completed by the sixth week of development. Both left and right umbilical veins
come in contact with the expanding liver and are tapped by the vitelline
sinusoids. Their blood flow is thereby diverted through the liver. The proximal portion of each vessel becomes obliterated and shortly thereafter the
entire right vein disappears. This leaves a single vessel to drain the placenta,
the:

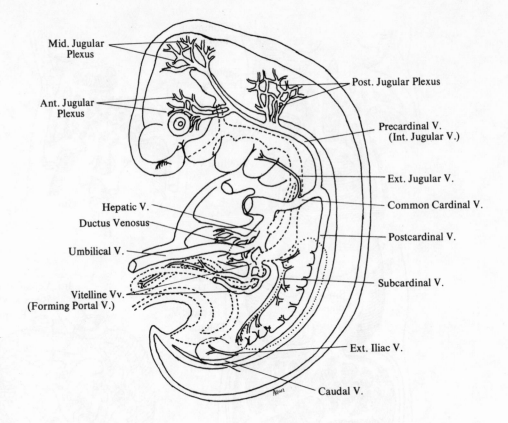

Mid. Jugular
Plexus

Ant. Jugular
Plexus

Post. Jugular Plexus

Precardinal V.
(Int. Jugular V.)

Ext. Jugular V.

Common Cardinal V.

Hepatic V.

Ductus Venosus

Postcardinal V.

Umbilical V.

Subcardinal V.

Vitelline Vv.
(Forming Portal V.)

Ext. Iliac V.

Caudal V.

FIGURE **32.** The venous system in a 10 mm. embryo (about 37 days) lateral view.

a. left umbilical vein–Blood passing through this vessel is diverted through the liver sinusoids due to the process of tapping and obliteration noted above. Certain of the hepatic sinusoids form the *hepatic veins* which drain the liver lobules whereas others enlarge to accommodate the blood from this vessel and form the:

b. *ductus venosus*–Since the base of the right vitelline vein is retained as the inferior vena cava which, via the hepatic veins, drains the liver, the most direct course to the heart for blood passing into the liver from the left umbilical vein is via the inferior vena cava. The ductus venosus, therefore, takes an oblique course, from left to right, through the liver to the inferior vena cava.

3. Cardinal system of veins–Modification or transformation of these vessels is a complex thing but can be resolved into two main processes. One of these is the change of the precardinal veins coincident with the shifting of the sinus venosus to the right side. The other process is the formation of the inferior vena cava. Transformation of the cardinal vessels is somewhat protracted, lagging behind the veins noted above, i.e. vitelline and umbilical, but it is essentially accomplished during the seventh week. (Figs. 32,33,34,35)

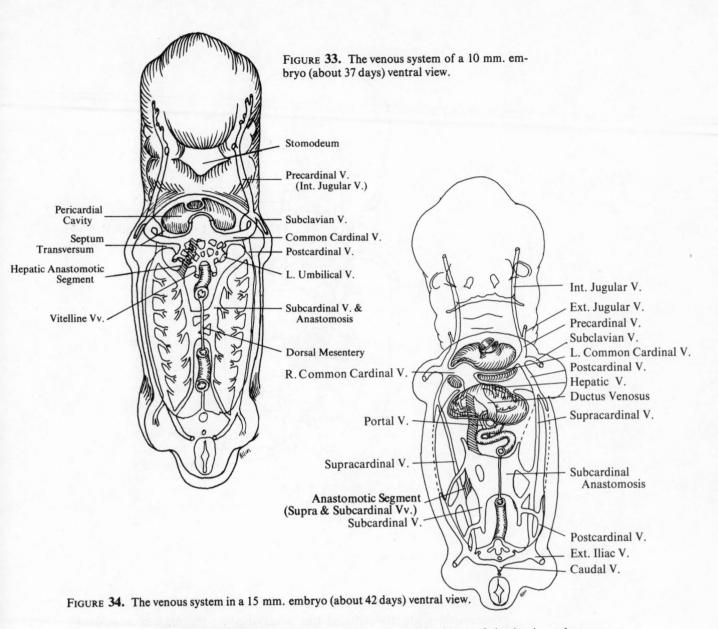

FIGURE **33.** The venous system of a 10 mm. embryo (about 37 days) ventral view.

Stomodeum

Precardinal V.
(Int. Jugular V.)

Pericardial Cavity

Subclavian V.

Common Cardinal V.

Septum Transversum

Postcardinal V.

Hepatic Anastomotic Segment

L. Umbilical V.

Vitelline Vv.

Subcardinal V. & Anastomosis

Dorsal Mesentery

R. Common Cardinal V.

Int. Jugular V.

Ext. Jugular V.

Precardinal V.

Subclavian V.

L. Common Cardinal V.

Postcardinal V.

Hepatic V.

Ductus Venosus

Supracardinal V.

Portal V.

Supracardinal V.

Subcardinal Anastomosis

Anastomotic Segment
(Supra & Subcardinal Vv.)

Subcardinal V.

Postcardinal V.

Ext. Iliac V.

Caudal V.

FIGURE **34.** The venous system in a 15 mm. embryo (about 42 days) ventral view.

a. precardinal veins–These vessels arise at the base of the brain, where they receive three tributary plexuses which drain that structure, and run caudally to join the common cardinal vessels. They receive the subclavian veins from the upper limbs. Distal to this juncture the vessels are retained as the *internal jugular veins*. During the eighth week an anastomosis between the two precardinal veins occurs. The bulk of the blood flow from the precardinal vein on the left is diverted through the anastomosis which becomes the *left brachiocephalic vein*. The right precardinal vein between the anastomosis and the subclavian-internal jugular junction becomes the *right brachiocephalic vein*. The terminal portion of the right precardinal and the right common cardinal vein are retained as the

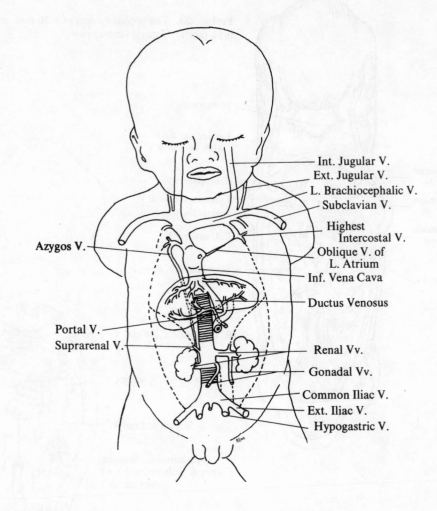

Int. Jugular V.
Ext. Jugular V.
L. Brachiocephalic V.
Subclavian V.
Highest
   Intercostal V.
Oblique V. of
   L. Atrium
Inf. Vena Cava
Ductus Venosus
Renal Vv.
Gonadal Vv.
Common Iliac V.
Ext. Iliac V.
Hypogastric V.

Azygos V.

Portal V.
Suprarenal V.

FIGURE 35. The venous system of the fetus.

superior vena cava. (Fig. 35) Below the anastomosis on the left, the precardinal is greatly reduced but is retained as the *highest intercostal vein.* As noted in the preceding chapter, the left common cardinal vein is retained as the *oblique vein* of the *left atrium.*

b. postcardinal veins—These vessels are formed by tributaries from the legs and caudal portion of the body, run dorsal to the mesonephric kidneys, and terminate in the common cardinal veins. They are supplanted by collateral channels to be discussed below. However, the *caudalmost portion* of the *inferior vena cava* and the *iliac veins* are derived from the caudal portions of the postcardinal veins. The cranialmost portion of the right postcardinal is retained as the stem of the *azygos vein.* The portions not mentioned above obliterate.

70

c. *subcardinal veins*–One set of the collateral channels noted above appears on the ventro-medial aspect of the mesonephros. These are the subcardinal veins which anastomose within the mesonephros with the postcardinal vessels and tap blood coming through them from the caudal portions of the body. An anastomosis develops between the sub-cardinals on each side which with a small portion of the right sub-cardinal just cranial to it, is retained as the *middle portion* of the *inferior vena cava* and some of the *renal, suprarenal*, and *gonadal veins*. (Fig. 35)

Cranially, the right subcardinal vein anastomoses with the hepatic portion (proximal portion of right vitelline vein) of the inferior vena cava by way of a ridge, the caval mesentery, extending from the right lobe of liver to the dorsal body wall. This anastomosis forms the plical portion of the inferior vena cava.

d. *supracardinal veins*–These veins constitute the second collateral channel noted above and appear dorsal to the mesonephros and essentially replace the postcardinal veins. They anastomose with the sub-cardinal veins, the anastomosis on the right becoming a part of the *inferior vena cava*. (Fig. 34,35) On the right side below the anastomosis the supracardinal forms an additional part of the inferior vena cava. Above the anastomosis with subcardinals, the right supracardinal vein becomes the *azygos vein*, whereas on the left it becomes the *hemiazygos vein*.

4. Inferior vena cava–To recapitulate, the inferior vena cava is formed by fusion of vessels of many origins which are listed below in craniocaudal sequence: (Fig. 35)

a. base of the right vitelline vein

b. plical portion formed by anastomosis of hepatic and subcardinal veins.

c. right subcardinal vein

d. supra-subcardinal anastomosis

e. right supracardinal vein

f. postcardinal veins

5. *Pulmonary veins*–These vessels arise as a simple branching sprout from the primitive atrium. With enlargement of the latter the base of the sprout is absorbed and its branches open separately into the chamber.

9

Fetal Circulation, Circulatory Changes at Birth, Lymph Vascular System

I. Fetal Circulation

The transformations of the primitive circulatory system require the major portion of the second month of development. At the end of that time, however, the pattern of fetal circulation is established. Only slight modifications occur during the subsequent months of intra-uterine life and these are essentially problems of growth and adaptation to local needs. Very little is known regarding the control of circulation in the fetus and one can only surmise that neurohumeral mechanisms similar to those effective in postnatal life may exert an influence. A description of the course of blood through the fetal circulatory system follows: (Figs. 30,36)

A. Arterial limb of circuit—Blood leaves the heart via two routes, the pulmonary trunk and the systemic aorta.

72

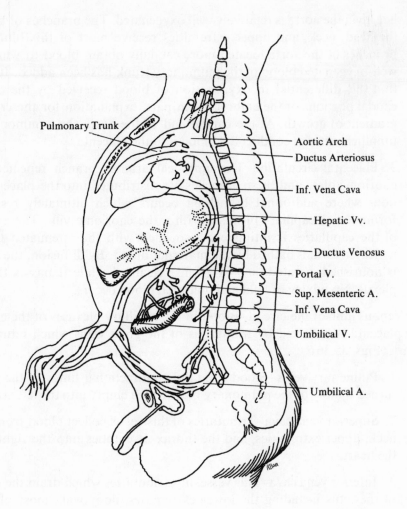

Pulmonary Trunk

Aortic Arch
Ductus Arteriosus

Inf. Vena Cava

Hepatic Vv.

Ductus Venosus

Portal V.

Sup. Mesenteric A.
Inf. Vena Cava

Umbilical V.

Umbilical A.

FIGURE **36.** Circulation of the fetus near term.

1. Pulmonary route–A small amount of the blood in the pulmonary trunk passes into the nonfunctional lungs via the pulmonary arteries. The bulk of it, however, bypasses the pulmonary system and, via the ductus arteriosus, passes into the descending thoracic aorta.

2. Systemic route–The blood which passes from the heart via the aorta is carried to all the tissues of the developing fetus and to the placental circulation as well. This is accomplished via the branches of the aorta noted in the last chapter. For reasons that will be explained below, blood leaving the

73

heart via the aorta is relatively well oxygenated. The branches of the aorta to the head, neck, and upper extremities receive most of this blood whereas branches of the aorta located more caudally obtain blood to which the less well-oxygenated blood of the pulmonary trunk has been added. It is thought that this differential in oxygenation of blood received by the cranial and caudal portions of the embryo is, in part, explanation for the craniocaudal gradient of growth. At the caudal end of the aorta the common iliac, then umbilical arteries conduct the blood into the placenta.

3. Placental circulation–The umbilical arteries branch repeatedly on the chorionic plate and these branches are distributed into the placental cotyledons where additional branching occurs which ultimately results in the formation of capillary plexuses within the chorionic villi. The endothelium of the capillaries is intimately associated with the attenuated trophoblast which, in turn, is bathed by the maternal blood. By diffusion, the fetal blood is nourished, aerated, and in a sense cleansed while it passes through the plexus. No mixing of fetal and maternal blood occurs.

B. Venous limb of the circuit–Blood in the capillary plexuses of the embryo and the placenta is collected by tributaries of the great veins which return it to the heart. (Figs. 35,36)

1. Pulmonary veins–Blood from the nonfunctional lungs of the fetus is returned by way of the pulmonary veins which empty into the left atrium.

2. Superior vena cava–Tributaries of this vessel collect blood from the head, neck, upper extremities, and the thorax. It empties into the right atrium of the heart.

3. Inferior vena cava–This vessel has tributaries which drain the caudal half of the fetus including the lower extremities, body wall, most of the pelvic viscera, kidneys, and adrenal glands. In addition, within the liver it receives blood from the hepatic veins which, in turn, received it from the portal vein. The inferior vena cava is also joined by the ductus venosus within the liver. The blood received from all these tributaries is emptied into the right atrium of the heart.

4. Portal vein–Blood from the gut is carried to the liver by the portal vein. Within the liver it passes into the hepatic veins, after traversing a system of sinusoids, and, as noted above, runs into the inferior vena cava.

5. Umbilical vein–The aerated, nourished, and cleansed blood from the placenta finds it way into the umbilical vein which enters the fetus via the umbilical cord. It runs cranially on the ventral body wall, within a fold of mesentery known as the falciform ligament, into the liver where it is continuous with the ductus venosus. Through the latter the umbilical vein blood passes into the inferior vena cava.

C. Movement of blood within the heart–The relatively well oxygenated blood from the inferior vena cava and the purely venous blood from the superior vena cava both enter the right atrium. They do not, however, become mixed to an appreciable extent. The flow from the inferior vena cava is directed toward the foramen ovale which is patent and permits passage into the left atrium. The valve of the foramen is held open due to the higher pressure within the right atrium. The bulk of the blood from the superior vena cava, on the other hand, passes through the right atrioventricular canal into the right ventricle. From the latter, blood passes out of the heart through the pulmonary trunk and into the pulmonary arteries or the ductus arteriosus as has been noted above. The relatively well oxygenated blood from the placental circuit which reaches the left atrium via the foramen ovale is mixed with the small venous return from the pulmonary veins. This blood then passes into the left ventricle and into the aorta. Thus blood to the aortic arch and the branches therefrom is rich in nutrients and oxygen. The blood that passes caudally into the descending aorta is mixed with the blood passing through the ductus arteriosus which is poorer in these characteristics.

II. Circulatory Changes at Birth

Coincident with delivery of the fetus a number of striking alterations in the fetal cardiovascular system occur. These changes are accomplished by the interaction of a number of factors working upon the structures developed within the fetus in anticipation of the changes necessitated by birth. Much is yet to be learned regarding these changes but at least the basic pattern is quite clear. (Fig. 37)

A. Placental circulation–As birth occurs and the umbilical cord is severed there is a virtually instantaneous closure of the umbilical vessels.

1. Umbilical arteries–There is an immediate and complete closure of these arteries due to a spasmodic contraction of the vascular musculature. This results in an increase in the aortic pressure due to decrease run-off via the placental circuit. More blood is available to the vascular plexuses supplied by the aorta. Anatomical obliteration of the umbilical arteries within the fetus results in the formation of the cord-like *lateral umbilical ligaments*.

2. Umbilical veins–When the placental inflow is cut off there is, of course, a simultaneous cessation of venous return via the umbilical vein. Constriction of the latter occurs and it is eventually replaced by a cord, the *ligamentum teres*, which represents the intra-embryonic remnant of the umbilical vein.

3. Ductus venosus–Cessation of blood flow from the placental circuit eliminates the flow of blood through the ductus venosus, and closure of that structure occurs with its eventual conversion into the *ligamentum venosum*.

75

The immediate result of these actions is the elimination of the source of oxygenated blood and, as a consequence, the fetus becomes temporarily *anoxic.*

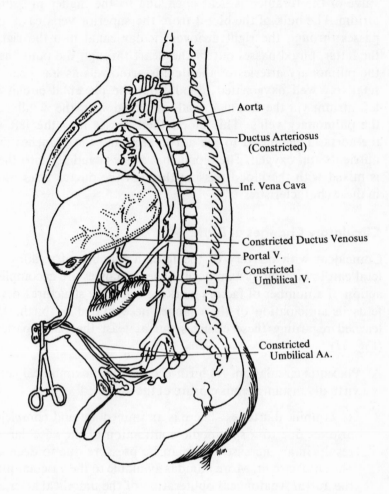

Aorta

Ductus Arteriosus (Constricted)

Inf. Vena Cava

Constricted Ductus Venosus

Portal V.

Constricted Umbilical V.

Constricted Umbilical Aа.

FIGURE **37.** Circulation in the newborn infant.

B. Pulmonary circulation–In order to alleviate the anoxia which develops upon separation of fetus and placenta, a new means of oxygenation is brought into being. The infant gasps, probably due to reflex response to anoxia, and the fetal lung, nonfunctional to this point, undertakes the expansion and modifications necessary to aerate the blood. With expansion of the lungs, coincidental expansion of the pulmonary circulatory system occurs.

76

1. Ductus arteriosus–Constriction of the ductus arteriosus occurs shortly after birth with the result that the blood leaving the right ventricle no longer bypasses the lungs. It is forced into the pulmonary arteries and their ramifications in the lung. The cause of closure (whether direct or indirect is not known) is relatively well established as being the elevation of the oxygen saturation of the blood. As the newborn infant gasps and breathes, the elevation occurs and the ductus closes. It is likely that the constriction is not absolutely maintained during the first few hours of life and that aortic blood can pass through the ductus into the pulmonary circuit. This would permit an additional exposure of the blood to oxygen and allow it to become saturated to a higher degree. Ultimately, however, anatomical obliteration of the ductus arteriosus converts it into the fibrous *ligamentum arteriosum*.

2. Pulmonary arteries–As noted above, with the expansion of the lungs and associated vascular bed, these vessels similarly expand to accommodate the increased blood flow through them.

3. Pulmonary veins–Throughout the fetal period these vessels conduct a trickle of blood from the lungs to the heart. At the onset of respiration and its correlated vascular changes the trickle is converted into a large flow and the vessels enlarge correspondingly.

C. Intracardiac changes–The pattern of blood flow through the heart is modified considerably at birth. All the blood entering the right atrium now has a low oxygen saturation. The increased run-off into the pulmonary trunk and lungs is effective in lowering the pressure on the right side of the heart. Conversely, increased aortic pressure and increased pulmonary venous return to the left atrium cause a relative elevation of pressures within the left side of the heart. This results in the functional closure of the foramen ovale followed by a fusion or structural closure of the valve (septum I) with the margins of the foramen (*limbus fossa ovalis* or *septum* II).

D. Circulation in the newborn infant–Following the changes described above, the definitive circulatory pattern of the postnatal individual is established. Venous blood from tributaries in the head, neck, upper extremities, and the thorax enters the right atrium via the superior vena cava. There it is mixed with blood from the inferior vena cava (no longer containing the oxygenated portion from the placenta) which has as its tributaries the hepatic (portal), renal, adrenal, gonadal, and common iliac veins. With each heartbeat blood in the right atrium is forced into the right ventricle and via the pulmonary trunk, is then conveyed to the pulmonary arteries. These, in turn, distribute it to the capillary plexuses of the lungs. The pulmonary veins return the now oxygenated blood to the left atrium and from the latter the blood passes into the left ventricle and then into the aorta which distributes it to all areas of the body.

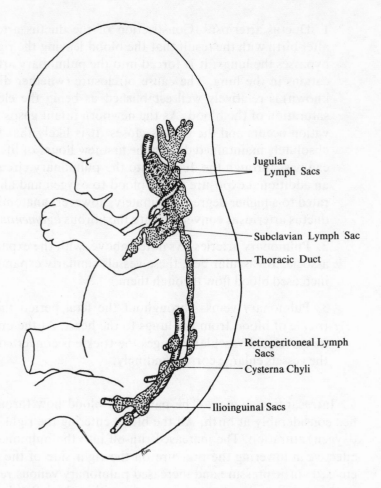

Jugular Lymph Sacs

Subclavian Lymph Sac

Thoracic Duct

Retroperitoneal Lymph Sacs

Cysterna Chyli

Ilioinguinal Sacs

FIGURE **38.** Fetal lymphatic system. (modified from Sabin)

III. Lymph Vascular System

A. Introduction–This is a one-way system consisting of endothelium lined vessels (lymphatics) which drain excess tissue fluid from the interstitial spaces and conduct that fluid back into the blood vascular system.

There are two theories regarding the origin of the lymphatic system. One suggests that the lymphatics are an outgrowth of the blood vascular system, especially the veins. The other, which is, perhaps, more plausible, describes the origin, like blood vessels, as mesenchymal clefts or spaces which become converted into vessels by the development of an endothelial lining. Coalescence of the isolated channels thus formed creates a network of lymphatic vessels. This system develops in intimate association with the venous system and connection with the latter is secondarily established. The primitive system is established at the end of the second month.

78

B. *Primitive lymph sacs*-These sacs, which consist of dilated portions of the lymphatic network, precede the establishment of the definitive system and are observed in three main areas: (Fig. 38)

1. *Jugular lymph sacs*-These sacs appear just lateral to the internal jugular veins. They are found bilaterally and receive branches from the cephalic portion of the embryo. They communicate inferiorly with the:

2. *Retroperitoneal lymph sac* and *the cysterna chyli*-These sacs lie at the base of the mesentery. Segments of their communications with the jugular sacs become converted into the unpaired *thoracic duct*. They drain the gut and its derivatives and also communicate caudally with the paired:

3. *Ilioinguinal lymph sacs*-These sacs are associated with the iliac veins and drain the lower part of the trunk and the lower extremities.

C. Elaboration of the primitive system-The union of the primitive sacs by longitudinal connections has been noted briefly above. This connection is specialized as the "trunk" vessel (*thoracic duct*) of the system and, via the left jugular sac, communicates with the venous system at the junction of the left internal jugular and subclavian veins. A similar communication on the right is established and a separate smaller trunk is formed which drains that side of the cephalic portion of the fetus. (Fig. 38) From the primitive lymphatic system new vessels develop and extend peripherally. These develop valves at intervals which direct the flow of the *lymph* or tissue fluid which enters the vessels by simple diffusion.

D. *Lymph glands* or *nodes*-During the third month of intrauterine development and in subsequent months, aggregations of lymphoid tissues appear in the lymphatic networks. In brief, this complex is converted into a lymph node with the peripheral (afferent) lymphatics conducting lymph to the node and the central (efferent) lymphatics carrying the lymph away from the node and, ultimately, into the thoracic duct. Within the node the lymph is, in essence, filtered and any particulate matter, etc., removed. In addition, lymphocytes are added to the lymph in variable numbers.

E. *Spleen*-Some question as to the advisability of including the development of the spleen at this point may be raised. However, because this organ is considered part of the lymphatic system, although little direct relation exists, it will be considered here.

The spleen develops somewhat like a lymph node. However, the development is within a (potential) blood vascular network. The latter is modified in that it consists of a large number of *sinuses* which develop independently of the blood vascular system but later become connected intimately. This process occurs between the layers of the *dorsal mesogastrium* (see Chapter 10). Later, development of lymphoid (white pulp) tissue associated with the arteries and erythroblastic (red pulp) tissue associated with the sinuses is observed. Eventually the blood is "filtered" by the spleen in a manner similar to the filtration of lymph by the lymph node.

10

Development and Rotation of the Gut

I.   Introduction

It should be recalled that the roof of the yolk sac (splanchnopleure) of late presomite and early somite embryos folds inward, i.e. dorsally into the embryo along the mid-axial line. This folding is essentially the result of the overgrowth of the lateral somatopleure. At the same time, however, growth of the embryo cranially and caudally results in the formation of the head and tail folds, respectively, which contain extensions or prolongations of the yolk sac. (Fig. 39) These changes result in the formation of the tubular gut. This is accomplished by the end of the fourth week. The fused ectoderm and endoderm of the buccopharyngeal (*oral*) and the cloacal membranes come to lie on the ventral aspects of the head and tail folds, respectively. The tubular gut gives origin to the digestive tract and the accessory organs of digestion. In addition, portions of the urinary tract arise from the caudal end of the gut.

The wall of the gut is formed by the bilaminar splanchnopleure. The mesodermal layer of the latter gives rise to the connective and muscular tissues of the gut, whereas the endodermal layer forms the epithelium lining of that structure and the parenchyma of organs which arise therefrom.

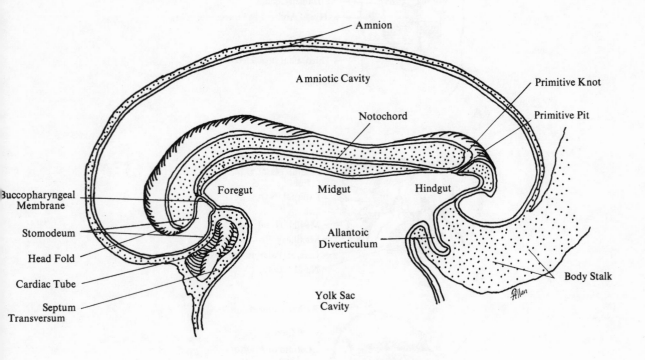

FIGURE 39. The primitive gut in an early somite embryo (mesoderm stippled).

II. Digestive Tract

Whereas the greatest portion of the definitive digestive tract is derived from the primitive gut, the cephalic end of the tract is derived from an external depression on the ventral aspect of the head fold. This depression is called the:

81

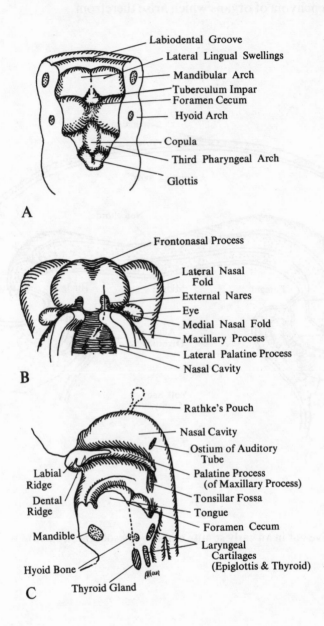

A

B

C

FIGURE **40.** Formation of the oral and nasal cavities and associated structures (at 10 mm., 37 days).
A. Floor of the oral cavity.
B. Roof of the oral (and part of nasal) cavity.
C. Midsaggital section.

82

A. Stomodeum–It is bounded superiorly by the head fold, *frontonasal process,* inferiorly and laterally by the mandibular or first branchial arch, and by the *maxillary process* between the two structures noted. In the floor of the depression, the oral membrane separates stomodeum from the foregut (pharynx). During the fourth week the membrane breaks down, permitting continuity between foregut and stomodeum. The line of demarcation of this union becomes increasingly difficult to identify as development proceeds and both foregut and stomodeum, especially the latter, contribute to the formation of the *oral* and *nasal cavities.* (Figs. 24,39,40,41,42)

1. Subdivision of the stomodeum–The stomodeum is divided into dorsal (nasal) and ventral (oral) halves by two bilaterally placed horizontal plates which grow medially from their origin from the maxillary processes on either side. These plates are called the:

a. *lateral palatine processes*–These processes meet and fuse in the midline and form the major portion of the definitive palate. Fusion takes place early in the third month of development. Prior to the isolation of the dorsal portion of the stomodeum as the nasal cavity, paired olfactory pits or sacs are formed in the head fold, more particularly the frontonasal process, overlying the stomodeum. Eventually they communicate with the latter and form the rostral or cephalic portion of the nasal cavity. The medial nasal processes which are located just medial to the pits fuse and, with a contribution from the roof of the primitive stomodeum, form the:

b. *nasal septum*–As the septum grows caudally and ventrally it meets and fuses with the palatine processes as they are completing their union. The medial nasal processes also contribute to the formation of the most cephalic portion of the palate via the small *medial palatine processes.*

2. *Tongue*–The tongue arises in the floor of the oral cavity from several anlagen. These anlagen include tissues derived from stomodeum and foregut. (Figs. 40,41,42) They appear at the end of the fourth week of development.

a. *lateral lingual swellings*–These swellings appear on either side of the midline and are derived from the mandibular arch. The major (rostral two-thirds) portion of the tongue is derived from these swellings.

b. *tuberculum impar*–This is a midline swelling located immediately caudal to the bilateral lingual swellings. It is retained in the body of the tongue.

c. *copula*–This is a midline swelling in the floor of the pharynx opposite the second branchial arch which, with contributions from the third and, perhaps, fourth branchial arches, forms the root of the tongue (caudal one-third).

83

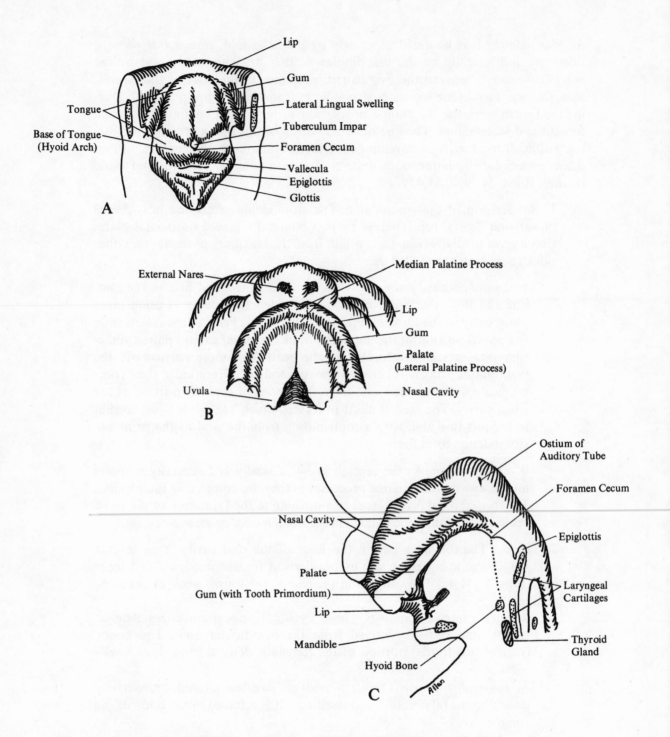

FIGURE **41.** Formation of oral and nasal cavities and associated structures (at 25 mm., 52 days).
A. Floor of the oral cavity.
B. Roof of the oral cavity.
C. Midsagittal section.

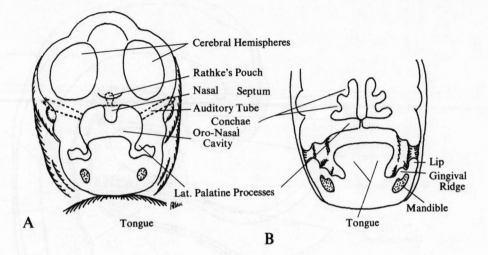

A   Tongue   B

Cerebral Hemispheres

Rathke's Pouch

Nasal   Septum

Auditory Tube

Conchae

Oro-Nasal
Cavity

Lip

Gingival
Ridge

Mandible

Lat. Palatine Processes

Tongue

FIGURE **42.** Frontal sections (diagrammatic) of the head at
A. 25 mm. (52 days). B. 44 mm. (67–70 days).

Fusion of these primordia and their enlargement to form the definitive tongue are virtually completed by the end of the second month.

B. *Foregut*–The cranial prolongation of the gut is known as the foregut which is subdivided soon after its formation into several segments: (Figs. 39,44)

1. *Pharynx*–The rostral end of the foregut is intimately related to the stomodeum and participates with the latter in the formation of the oral and nasal cavities. The pharynx is lined with endoderm and is bounded laterally and inferiorly by the:

a. *pharyngeal* (*branchial* or *visceral*) *arches*–These are mesenchymal bars or cores formed during the fourth week of development which are covered externally by ectoderm and internally by the endoderm of the pharynx. Lateral evaginations of the endoderm occur between adjacent arches and constitute the:

b. *pharyngeal* (*branchial* or *visceral*) *pouches*–These are numbered from rostral to caudal with the first pouch located between the first and second pharyngeal arches. Between each of the arches externally an invagination of the ectoderm constitutes the:

c. *external* (*pharyngeal*) *clefts*–The clefts are numbered in the same manner as the pouches. The caudal three clefts and arches become depressed somewhat and form the *cervical sinus*. (Fig. 23)

The pharynx is also intimately related to the pericardial swelling ventrally and extends caudally to a point opposite the sixth pharyngeal arch where it is grooved ventrally by the *laryngotracheal groove* and is continuous with the:

85

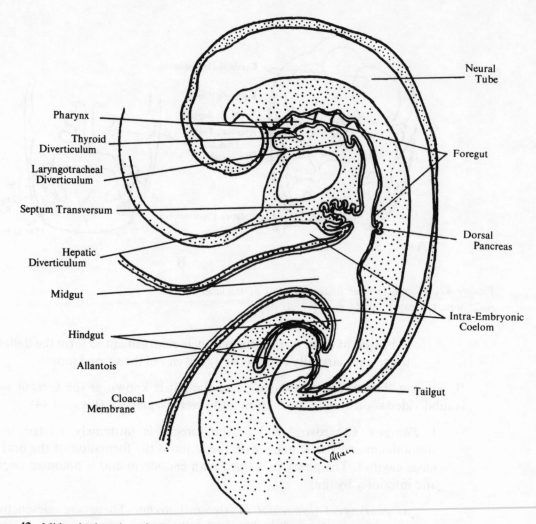

Pharynx

Thyroid
Diverticulum

Laryngotracheal
Diverticulum

Septum Transversum

Hepatic
Diverticulum

Midgut

Hindgut

Allantois

Cloacal
Membrane

Neural
Tube

Foregut

Dorsal
Pancreas

Intra-Embryonic
Coelom

Tailgut

FIGURE **43.** Midsagittal section of a 5 mm. embryo (32 days). (mesoderm stippled)

2. *Esophagus*–This segment is formed in the fourth week and passes caud-ally, dorsal to the pericardial cavity and its contents, and is closely as-sociated with the ventral *trachea* which arises as a diverticulum of the pharynx. (Fig. 44) It continues through the *septum transversum* where it is continuous with the:

3. *Stomach*–This is a short segment near the caudal end of the foregut. It is attached to the dorsal and ventral body walls by the dorsal and ventral mesogastria. As development proceeds it becomes in the fifth week of de-velopment flattened by the more rapid growth of the dorsal border. The re-sult is a flattened tube which has a *greater* (dorsal) *curvature* and a *lesser* (ventral) *curvature*. Rotation and transposition of the gut, especially its more caudal portions, during the sixth and seventh weeks modify the orig-inal position of the stomach considerably.

86

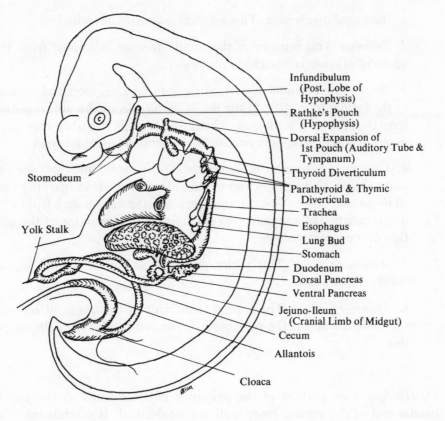

Infundibulum
(Post. Lobe of
Hypophysis)

Rathke's Pouch
(Hypophysis)

Dorsal Expansion of
1st Pouch (Auditory Tube &
Tympanum)

Thyroid Diverticulum

Parathyroid & Thymic
Diverticula

Trachea

Esophagus

Lung Bud

Stomach

Duodenum

Dorsal Pancreas

Ventral Pancreas

Jejuno-Ileum
(Cranial Limb of Midgut)

Cecum

Allantois

Cloaca

Stomodeum

Yolk Stalk

FIGURE **44.** Midsagittal section of a 10 mm. embryo (37 days).

4. *Duodenum*–This segment includes the terminal portion of the foregut and the beginning of the midgut. From it arise the diverticula of the liver and pancreas. The duodenum remains a simple tube which, also due to rotation of the gut, etc., eventually becomes fused to the posterior abdominal wall.

C. *Midgut*–At first the midgut is in open communication with the yolk sac but with closure of the ventral body wall during the latter part of the third week of development the communication is reduced to the narrowed *yolk stalk*. (Fig. 43) The latter becomes detached during the fifth week. At the same time, the gut lengthens rapidly and forms a loop which later (seventh week) herniates into the extra-embryonic coelom in the umbilical cord. The midgut has a dorsal mesentery which is carried with it during the herniation process. The loop of the gut has a cranial segment and a caudal segment which twist upon one another in a counterclockwise manner (when looking at the ventral aspect of the embryo). This twisting occurs as the gut returns to the abdominal cavity from its herniated condition. The midgut is divided into: (Fig. 44)

87

1. Terminal duodenum–This segment is continuous with the:

2. *Jejunum*–This portion of the small intestine is derived from the cranial segment of the herniated loop of the gut.

3. *Ileum*–This segment is derived from the cranial loop and a small portion of the caudal loop. It is to the ileum derived from the apical portion of the loop that the yolk stalk is attached. *Meckel's diverticulum* may occur in this position and the stalk may occasionally remain patent or cystic.

4. *Cecum* and *vermiform appendix*–The caudal limb of the midgut is marked by a slight projection or dilation at five weeks marking the junction of ileum and *colon*. This dilation becomes the cecum and from it a tubular diverticulum, the appendix, takes origin. The remainder of the caudal portion of the loop forms the:

5. *Ascending colon*–This with the cecum and more caudal segments constitute the *large intestine*.

6. *Transverse colon*–The cranial two-thirds of this segment is formed from the midgut whereas the remainder is formed by the cranialmost portion of the:

D. *Hindgut*–This portion of the primitive gut is formed as the tail fold and caudal end of the ventral body wall are established. It extends into the caudal portion of the embryo and terminates, for practical purposes, at the point where the endoderm of the gut and the ectoderm of the body wall fuse to form the cloacal membrane. It is divided into these segments:

1. Terminal one-third of transverse colon–This portion is drawn into the cranial end of the abdominal cavity.

2. *Descending colon*–This portion runs caudally and is continuous with the:

3. *Pelvic colon*–This segment is ultimately divided into the *sigmoid colon* and the *rectum*. In earlier stages, however, it is represented by the dilated, blindly ending:

4. *Cloaca* (Fig. 44)–This structure ultimately (late in the sixth week) gives rise to the:

   a. rectum–Terminal portion of the digestive tube.

   b. *urogenital sinus* and its derivatives–These will be described in detail with the genital and urinary systems.

5. *Tail gut*–This is a small and rudimentary portion of the gut in the tail fold which disappears in the fifth week of development.

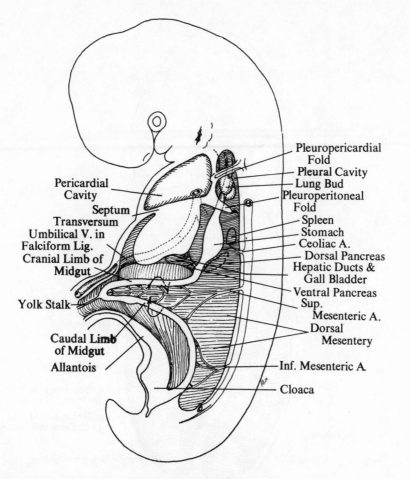

Pleuropericardial
Fold
Pleural Cavity
Lung Bud
Pleuroperitoneal
Fold
Spleen
Stomach
Ceoliac A.
Dorsal Pancreas
Hepatic Ducts &
Gall Bladder
Ventral Pancreas
Sup.
Mesenteric A.
Dorsal
Mesentery
Inf. Mesenteric A.
Cloaca

Pericardial
Cavity
Septum
Transversum
Umbilical V. in
Falciform Lig.
Cranial Limb of
Midgut
Yolk Stalk
Caudal Limb
of Midgut
Allantois

FIGURE **45.** Mesenteries of the 10 mm. embryo (37 days) lateral view.

III. Rotation of the Gut and Transposition of Its Mesenteries

A. *Dorsal mesentery*-The gut is suspended from the dorsal body wall by the continuous curtain-like dorsal mesentery through which vessels and nerves reach the gut. That portion supporting the stomach is called the *mesogastrium,* that portion supporting the duodenum, the *mesoduodenum*, and so forth.

B. *Ventral mesentery*-The gut is connected to the ventral body wall only at the cranial end of the intra-abdominal portion by the ventral mesogastrium. The latter is intimately associated with the developing liver and will be treated in more detail elsewhere.

C. Rotation-As development of the gut and its several segments proceeds, elongation of each segment occurs much more rapidly than that of the dorsal body wall from which it is suspended. Hence the dorsal mesentery becomes relatively expanded at its attachment to the gut and much more restricted at its attachment to the body wall. (Figs. 45,46) As noted above, the enlarging gut

89

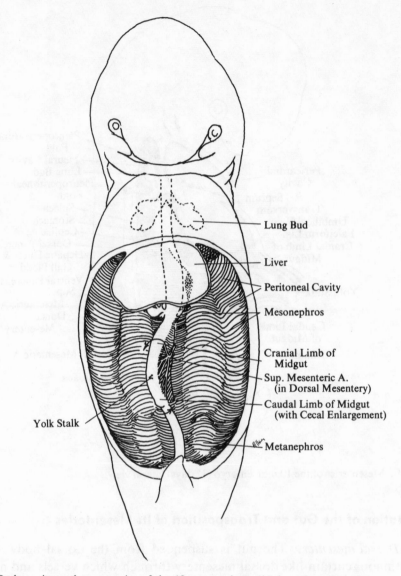

Lung Bud

Liver

Peritoneal Cavity

Mesonephros

Cranial Limb of
Midgut

Sup. Mesenteric A.
(in Dorsal Mesentery)

Caudal Limb of Midgut
(with Cecal Enlargement)

Yolk Stalk

Metanephros

FIGURE 46. Body cavity and mesenteries of the 10 mm. embryo (37 days) lateral view.

overflows the abdominal cavity into the exocoelom of the umbilical cord, carrying the expanded mesentery with it. Just prior to and during the herniation, the portion of the gut destined to be stomach rotates in its long axis and turns its left side toward the ventral body wall and the right side toward the dorsal body wall. Each segment of the gut and its mesentery will be discussed separately.

1. Stomach–As has been noted above, the stomach rotates on its longitudinal axis and as its greater and lesser curvatures develop it assumes a position in the upper-left quadrant of the abdominal cavity. As a consequence the greater curvature is directed toward the left and inferiorly. (Fig. 47)

90

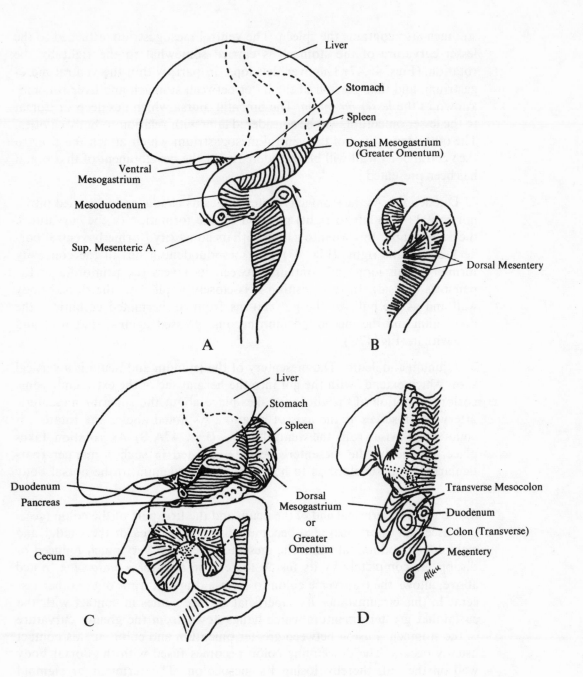

FIGURE **47.** Transposition of the mesenteries. A, B, and C. Ventral views. D. Lateral view (from left).

The dorsal mesogastrium attached to the greater curvature is therefore carried in these directions and continues to enlarge so that a sheet of excess mesogastrium forms which drapes over the rest of the viscera and constitutes the *greater omentum.* That portion of the greater omentum to the left of the

91

stomach also contains the spleen. The ventral mesogastrium attached to the lesser curvature of the stomach is carried somewhat to the right by the rotation. (Figs. 46,47) The liver develops, in part, within the ventral mesogastrium, and that portion of the latter between stomach and liver becomes known as the *lesser omentum*. The omental bursa,which lies deep or dorsal to the lesser omentum, will be considered later with relation to body cavities. The other derivatives of the ventral mesogastrium which attach the liver to the ventral body wall will be considered after the development of that organ has been presented.

2. Duodenum–As the stomach rotates and as its caudal end is carried into a horizontal (from left to right) position by the formation of the curvatures, the duodenum is thrown into a loop with its convexity (formerly ventral border) toward the right. (Fig. 47) The mesoduodenum lies in the concavity formed by this loop and contains between its layers the primordia of the pancreas (dorsal). In this position it is closely applied to the dorsal body wall and as the bulk of the gut returns from its herniated condition, the duodenum and the mesoduodenum become pressed against that wall and fuse with it. (Fig. 47C)

3. Jejunum and ileum–The mesentery of the jejunum and ileum is a vertical sheet which extends with the gut into the hernial sac of the extra-embryonic coelom. Rotation of the gut loop takes place about the superior mesenteric artery which serves as the axis of rotation. As noted above, the rotation is counterclockwise from the ventral view. (Fig. 47A,B) As rotation takes place, obviously, the mesentery becomes twisted in such a manner (particularly the mesocolon) as to help affix the duodenum to the dorsal body wall.

4. Colon–The terminal end of the ileum and the first part of the colon (cecal and ascending portions) also become affixed to an area of the caudal and right dorsal abdominal wall. The mesentery becomes very much reduced or disappears completely by its fusion there. The *transverse mesocolon,* noted above, allows the transverse colon to form a drape in front of the other viscera. In this circumstance its superficial surface comes in contact with the curtainlike greater omentum which hangs down from the greater curvature of the stomach. Fusion between greater omentum and colon at this contact usually occurs. The descending colon becomes fused with the dorsal body wall on the left, thereby losing its mesocolon. The terminal or sigmoid colon has a simple mesocolon which allows this portion of the gut a certain mobility. The rectum, on the other hand, is closely applied to the dorsal wall of the pelvic cavity by its peritoneal reflections.

11

Development of the Gut Continued: Derivatives of the Stomodeum and Primitive Pharynx; Development of the Accessory Organs of Digestion

I. Introduction

As noted in the foregoing chapter, the stomodeum is a depression on the ventral aspect of the head fold and intimately related to the pharynx which is derived from the cephalic end of the foregut; bounded dorsally essentially by tissues of the head fold; laterally by the pharyngeal arches, with their intervening pouches; inferiorly by the fusion of the arches over the bulging pericardial cavity. Glandular derivatives of the primitive pharynx and the remainder of the gut are formed by evaginations of the endoderm which extend into the mesenchyme of the pharyngeal arch or splanchnopleure of the gut. The derivatives of the stomodeum and gut will be considered cephalocaudally.

II. Stomodeal Derivatives (Fig. 48)

A. *Rathke's pouch*–At the end of the fourth week, the primordium of the *anterior lobe* of the *hypophysis* or *pituitary body* arises as a tubular evagination from the dorsal wall of the primitive oral cavity at a point near the site of the former buccopharyngeal or stomodeal membrane. It is difficult to determine therefore whether the cellular components of the diverticulum are ectodermal or endodermal in nature, although origin from the former seems most likely. As it approximates the diencephalon of the brain the diverticulum is met by an evagination, the *infundibulum*, which gives rise to the *posterior lobe* and *stalk of the hypophysis*. Ultimately, at eight weeks, the connection of the pouch with the pharynx becomes obliterated although remnants of the tissue at the site of evagination sometimes form a *pharyngeal hypophysis*.

B. Oral and nasal cavities–The formation of these cavities is described in the preceding chapter.

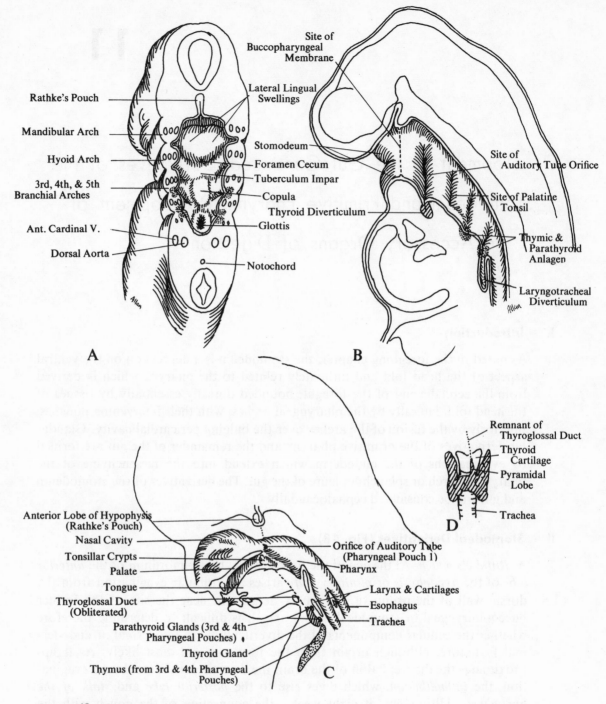

Rathke's Pouch

Mandibular Arch

Hyoid Arch

3rd, 4th, & 5th
Branchial Arches

Ant. Cardinal V.

Dorsal Aorta

Site of
Buccopharyngeal
Membrane

Lateral Lingual
Swellings

Stomodeum

Foramen Cecum

Tuberculum Impar

Copula

Thyroid Diverticulum

Glottis

Notochord

Site of
Auditory Tube Orifice

Site of Palatine
Tonsil

Thymic &
Parathyroid
Anlagen

Laryngotracheal
Diverticulum

A

B

Remnant of
Thyroglossal Duct

Thyroid
Cartilage

Pyramidal
Lobe

Trachea

D

Anterior Lobe of Hypophysis
(Rathke's Pouch)

Nasal Cavity

Tonsillar Crypts

Palate

Tongue

Thyroglossal Duct
(Obliterated)

Parathyroid Glands (3rd & 4th
Pharyngeal Pouches)

Thyroid Gland

Thymus (from 3rd & 4th Pharyngeal
Pouches)

Orifice of Auditory Tube
(Pharyngeal Pouch 1)

Pharynx

Larynx & Cartilages

Esophagus

Trachea

C

FIGURE 48. Pharyngeal derivatives.
A. Dorsal view (dorsal wall of pharynx removed). Parathyroids and thymus stippled, thyroid cross hatched.
B. Lateral view.
C. Lateral view of near term fetus.
D. Ventral view of thyroid gland.

94

III. Derivatives of the Pharynx (Figs. 40,41,42,48)

A. Pharyngeal pouches–The endodermal lining of each pouch is the tissue of importance in considering the derivatives of the pouch. However, the contributions of the surrounding mesenchyme to the capsule and stroma of the organs derived from the pouches should be remembered. The various derivatives follow in the same order as the pouches giving them origin.

1. *Middle ear cavity* and the *auditory* (*Eustachian*) *tube*–These structures are derived from the cavity of the dorsal portion of the *first pharyngeal pouch* and are lined with the endoderm of that pouch. These derivatives are not distinguishable until the eighth week.

2. *Tonsillar crypts*–The crypts were thought to be derived from the *second pharyngeal pouch*, but recent evidence indicates that the pouch plays no part in their formation.

3. *Parathyroid glands*–These glands take origin from ventral portions of both the *third* and *fourth pharyngeal pouches*, usually one gland from each pouch. The primordia appear in the sixth week and migrate ventrally and medially to become associated with the thyroid gland during the seventh week. The glands from the third pouch are carried with the thyroid in its caudal migration so that in the adult they come to lie below or caudal to those from the fourth pouch.

4. *Thymus*–This gland takes origin bilaterally from the *third* and *fourth pouches* and, at the same time as the parathyroids, also migrates ventromedially and caudally to lie eventually at the base of the neck and in the upper thorax. The paired diverticula are formed by epithelial cords which are later replaced or infiltrated by lymphoid tissue (12 weeks).

5. Ultimobranchial body–This is a small, short-lived diverticulum from the fifth pharyngeal pouch which has no known function. However, it has been suggested by some that this tissue becomes incorporated into the thyroid gland.

B. Derivatives of the pharynx proper (Fig. 48)

1. Tongue–This has already been considered in Chapter 10.

2. *Thyroid gland*–This organ arises as a midline diverticulum which is to be found between the fused portions of the first and second pharyngeal arches, that is, between the anterior two-thirds and posterior one-third of the definitive tongue. The site of the diverticulum is marked by the *foramen cecum* of the adult. From its origin the diverticulum extends caudally, closely associated with the ventral aspect of the pharynx, then the larynx and trachea, to which it is closely applied throughout the remainder of development. The intimate association with the parathyroid glands is noted above, and the

95

possibility exists that additional thyroid tissue is derived from other pharyngeal pouches, especially the fourth. Frequently a trail of thyroid tissue is left along the course followed by the primordium and constitutes small accumulations of *accessory thyroid tissue*. The apex of the *pyramidal lobe* of the adult gland is sometimes connected to the foramen cecum by a strand of tissue marking the course of the gland. If this tissue retains a lumen, as is often the case, it is known as a *thyroglossal duct*.

3. *Laryngotracheal groove*–This is a ventral diverticulum which gives rise to the respiratory tree–to be considered in detail later in this chapter.

IV. Caudal Portion of Foregut

A. *Hepatic diverticulum* (Figs. 43,44,49)–This diverticulum evaginates early in the fourth week from the caudal portion of the foregut (near the anterior intestinal portal) and grows ventrally into the ventral mesentery and the septum transversum. This constitutes the hepatic primordium from which the *liver, gall bladder* and associated ducts are derived. The primordium grows rapidly in the substance of the septum transversum, breaking up the primitive venous channels found therein en route to the heart, into the hepatic sinusoids. In the sixth week it divides into several main portions, which later become the *lobes* of the liver. The *cystic diverticulum* passes from the main diverticulum and forms the gall bladder and its duct. As these organs develop they carry the mesothelium of the peritoneal lining before them. Indeed, the gall bladder and liver become apparently located between the layers of the lesser omentum (ventral mesogastrium). Actually the liver also draws away from the caudal surface of the septum transversum somewhat, carrying the peritoneal membrane from the latter with it. (Figs. 45,47) The reflection of peritoneum over the liver is known as the *fibrous perivascular* (*Glisson's*) *capsule*, and the reflections from the liver to the septum (later *diaphragm*) constitute the *coronary, triangular*, and *falciform ligaments*. The last carries the umbilical vein from the ventral body wall into the liver substance. The differentiation and specialization of the hepatic primordium into the functional, bile-producing liver cords is apparently complete by the twelfth week.

B. Pancreatic diverticula (Figs. 44,45,49)

1. *Ventral pancreas*–This diverticulum arises from the duodenum closely associated with the hepatic diverticulum and, due to absorption of some of the gut wall into the latter, eventually is noted as a branch of the hepatic diverticulum. The pancreatic primordium represented by this diverticulum grows into the *ventral mesoduodenum* (mesogastrium). Later it is carried by differential growth of the gut wall into a position to the right, then dorsal to the gut where it contacts the second pancreatic primordium. (Fig. 49)

96

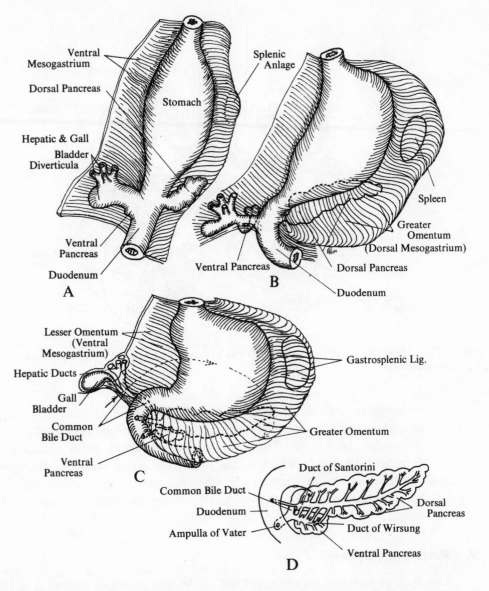

FIGURE **49.** Rotation of the stomach and changes in associated structures (ventral views). A. At 7 mm. (34 days). B. At 10 mm. (37 days). C. At 15 mm. (42 days). D. Definitive relationships of pancreas.

2. *Dorsal pancreas*–This primordium arises as a separate diverticulum from the dorsal border of the duodenum and extends into the dorsal mesoduodenum (mesogastrium). Its dorsal extremity or tail ultimately reaches nearly to the spleen. As the ventral pancreatic primordium is brought into position just caudal to that portion of the dorsal pancreas nearest the gut, fusion takes place. (Fig. 49) The duct of each diverticulum drains the portion of the organ which developed in association with it. However, the *ventral duct* (*duct of Wirsung*) taps the *duct* of the *dorsal pancreas* (*duct of Santorrini*) and becomes

97

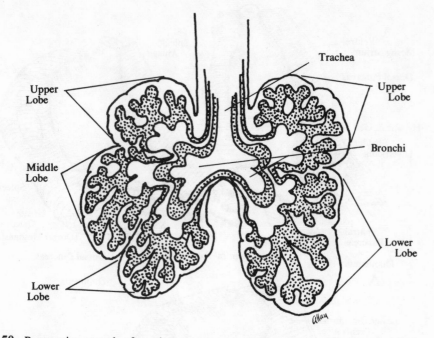

FIGURE **50.** Progressive growth of respiratory tree at stages from 6 mm. (33 days) internally to 15 mm. (42 days) externally.

the *definitive duct* which then empties with the duct of the hepatic primordium (*common bile duct*) via a small dilated duct (*ampulla of Vater*) which enters the duodenum. The glandular tissue arises from branches of the diverticula, some of which retain their association with the ducts and are, thereby, exocrine in function and elaborate the pancreatic enzymes. The rest become disassociated with the ducts and form the endocrine *islets of Langerhans.*

V.   Respiratory System

This system arises as an outpouching of the gut as noted above. It is lined by endoderm which carries before it a layer of mesenchyme which later gives rise to the connective and muscular elements of its wall.

A. *Laryngotracheal groove*–This groove appears in the ventral midline of the pharynx between the bases of the fifth and sixth pharyngeal arches. The latter arches with the fourth arch contribute to both the skeleton (cartilaginous) and the musculature of the: (Figs. 40,41,48)

1. Larynx–This organ is formed in the position just noted by the *in situ* formation of a musculocartilaginous "box" lined with endoderm, which guards the entrance to the respiratory tree. Contributions from the various pharyngeal arches to the larynx are as follows:

98

a. fourth pharyngeal arch–This arch gives rise to the *epiglottic, thyroid,* and *cuneiform cartilages* of the larynx and associated muscles.

b. fifth (and sixth) pharyngeal arches–These give origin to the *arytenoid, corniculate,* and *cricoid cartilages* and associated muscles.

2. *Trachea*–This is a caudal extension of the laryngotracheal groove which is tubular and located in the dorsal wall of the pericardial cavity. The tracheal primordium extends caudally and bifurcates into the paired *primary bronchi* which, clothed by mesenchyme and the mesothelial lining of coelom, bulge from the dorsal wall of the coelom (pleuroperitoneal portion) and constitute the:

3. *Lung buds*–Repeated growth and division of the primary bronchi within the lung buds result in the formation of the right and left *lungs* and their component lobes and lobules. Terminally the bronchi (now *bronchioles*) form the potential *alveoli* which, with other segments of the system, remain relatively small until birth when they undergo expansion. (Fig. 50)

99

12

Body Cavities and Mesenteries

I. Body Cavities (Figs. 51,52,53,54,55,56)

A. Introduction and review–The inverted U-shaped cleft in the mesoderm of the late presomite embryo noted in an earlier chapter constitutes the primitive intra-embryonic coelom. The cleft crosses the midline in front of the head fold and prochordal plate. The two limbs of the U extend caudally along the lateral sides of the somites and communicate at their caudal extremities with the extra-embryonic coelom at the margins of the embryonic disc. (Fig. 51) The coelom is bounded externally, i.e. dorsally or toward the amniotic cavity, by the somato-pleure and its floor is formed by the splanchnopleure which, in turn, forms the roof of the yolk sac. The cardiogenic area is found in the floor of the cranial portion of the coelom.

B. Division of the primitive coelom–The primitive coelom is arbitrarily divided into several areas which are subsequently divided by actual partitions or septa.

1. *Pericardial area*–This portion of the coelom is adjacent to the cardio-genic plate, i.e. anterior to the prochordal plate, and is carried caudally and ventrally as the head fold develops. It assumes a position ventral to the branchial region of the embryo and as development proceeds eventually shifts still more caudally into the thoracic region. (Fig. 52)

2. *Pleuroperitoneal cavities*–The paired limbs of the U-shaped coelom constitute these cavities, each of which becomes subdivided into cranial and caudal portions. (Figs. 53,54)

a. *pleural cavity*–This is the cranial segment of the limb which communicates freely with the lateral extremity of the pericardial cavity. (Fig. 55)

b. *peritoneal cavity*–This is the caudal segment of the limb which originally communicates with the extra-embryonic coelom. As the definition of the embryo's ventral body wall is completed this communication is reduced to a small cavity within the umbilical cord.

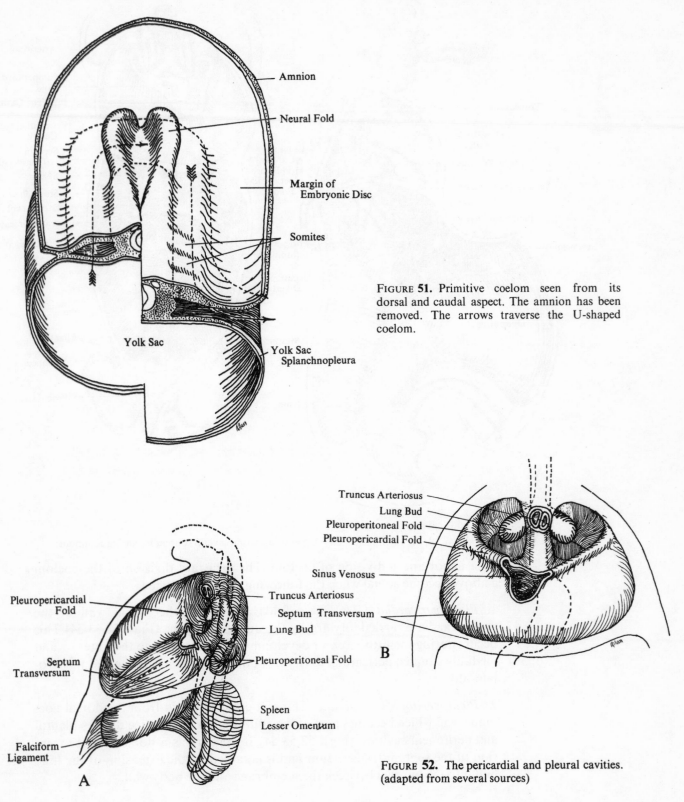

Amnion

Neural Fold

Margin of
Embryonic Disc

Somites

Yolk Sac

Yolk Sac
Splanchnopleura

FIGURE 51. Primitive coelom seen from its
dorsal and caudal aspect. The amnion has been
removed. The arrows traverse the U-shaped
coelom.

Truncus Arteriosus
Lung Bud
Pleuroperitoneal Fold
Pleuropericardial Fold

Sinus Venosus

Septum Transversum

B

Pleuropericardial
Fold

Truncus Arteriosus

Septum
Transversum

Lung Bud

Pleuroperitoneal Fold

Spleen
Lesser Omentum

Falciform
Ligament

A

FIGURE 52. The pericardial and pleural cavities.
(adapted from several sources)

101

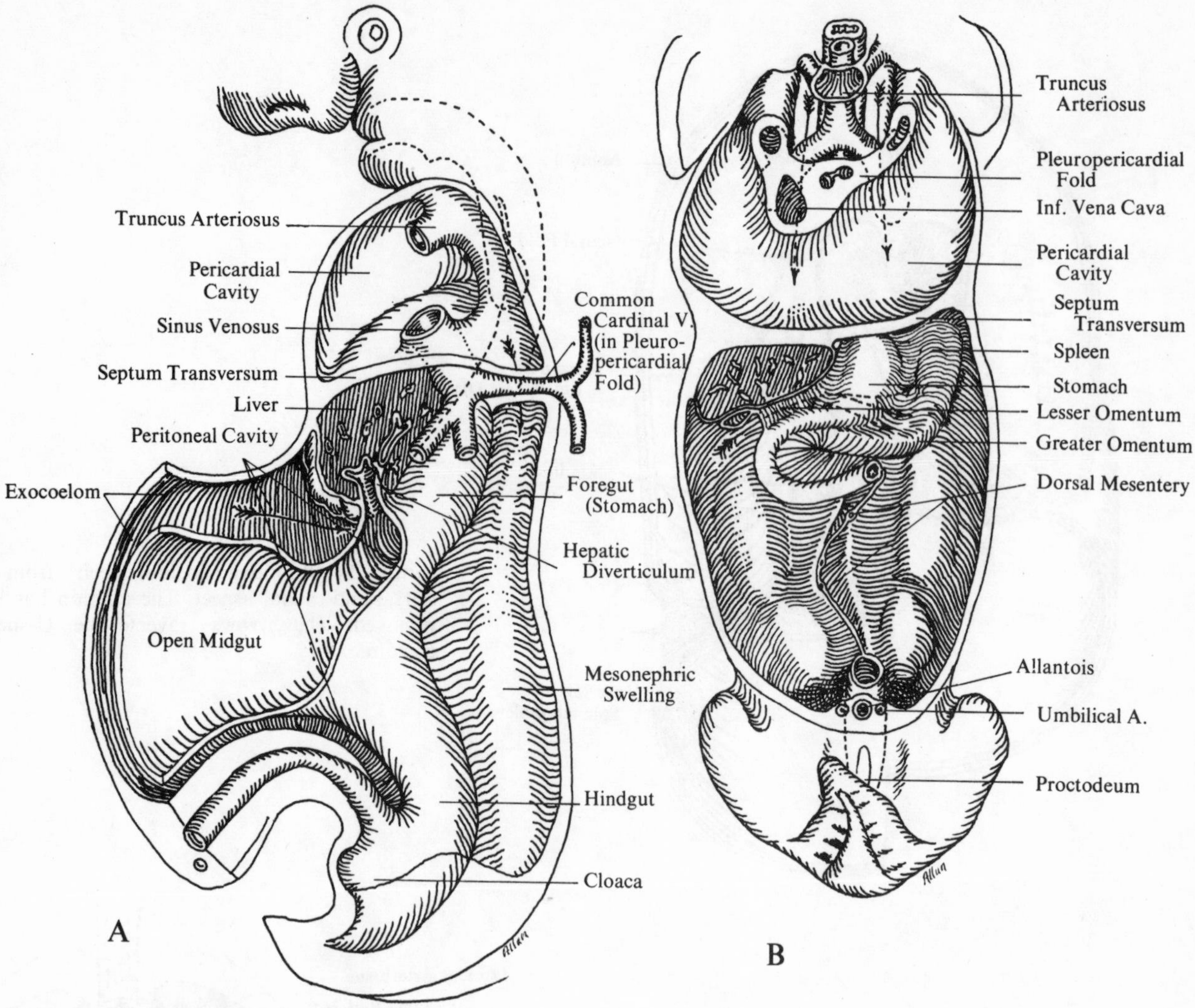

Truncus Arteriosus
Pericardial Cavity
Sinus Venosus
Septum Transversum
Liver
Peritoneal Cavity
Exocoelom
Open Midgut
Common Cardinal V. (in Pleuro-pericardial Fold)
Foregut (Stomach)
Hepatic Diverticulum
Mesonephric Swelling
Hindgut
Cloaca
A
Truncus Arteriosus
Pleuropericardial Fold
Inf. Vena Cava
Pericardial Cavity
Septum Transversum
Spleen
Stomach
Lesser Omentum
Greater Omentum
Dorsal Mesentery
Allantois
Umbilical A.
Proctodeum
B

FIGURE **53.** The body cavities.

A. At 3 mm. (28 days). B. At 10 mm. (37 days). (adapted from several sources including Kollman)

C. Septa important in division of coelom–The arbitrary division of the coelom noted above become actual when the following septa are formed:

1. *Pleuropericardial folds*–These folds arise from the dorsal wall of the coelom and are carried forward by the ducts of Cuvier. (Figs. 52,53,54) This occurs during the fifth week of development. They separate the anterior and medially situated pericardial cavity from the pleural cavities located postero-laterally.

2. *Pleuroperitoneal membrane*–This is a crescentic fold from the dorsal coelomic wall which becomes part of the adult diaphragm, hence divides pleural and peritoneal cavities. (Figs. 52,53,54) It appears as a dorso-lateral extension of the septum transversum and is enlarged by the extension of the lung bud into the interval between the membrane and the body wall.

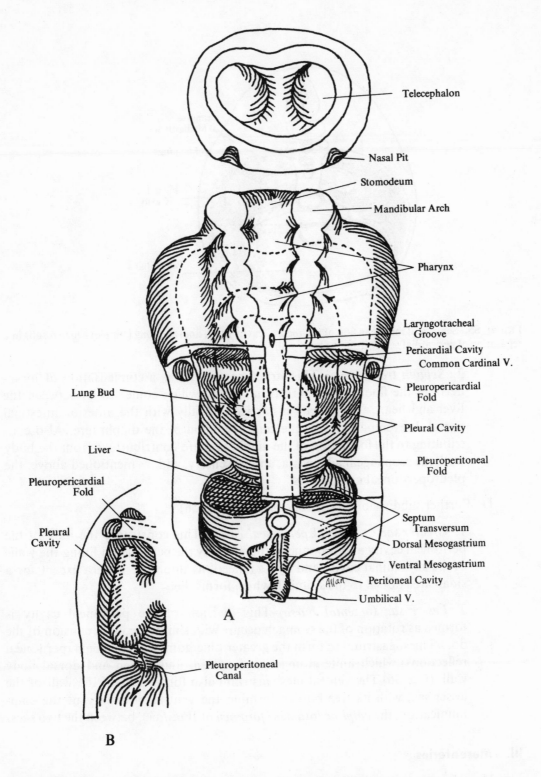

Telecephalon

Nasal Pit

Stomodeum

Mandibular Arch

Pharynx

Laryngotracheal Groove

Pericardial Cavity

Common Cardinal V.

Pleuropericardial Fold

Lung Bud

Pleural Cavity

Liver

Pleuroperitoneal Fold

Pleuropericardial Fold

Pleural Cavity

Septum Transversum

Dorsal Mesogastrium

Ventral Mesogastrium

Peritoneal Cavity

Umbilical V.

A

B

Pleuroperitoneal Canal

FIGURE **54.** Schema of the body cavities with dorsal half of embryo removed. Note arrow passing through pericardial and pleural cavities (A). The pleural cavity and pleuroperitoneal canal are shown.

103

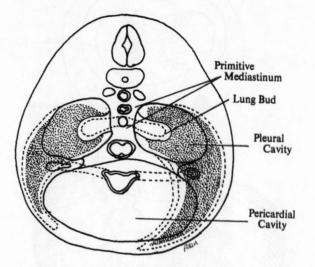

Primitive
Mediastinum

Lung Bud

Pleural
Cavity

Pericardial
Cavity

FIGURE **55.** Schema of the expansion of the pleural cavity (dash line) and lung (stipple) which results in a separation of pericardial cavity from the body wall.

3. *Septum transversum*–This structure appears as a condensation of mesoderm in the floor of the pericardial cavity which comes to lie between the liver and heart as the heart is carried caudally with the anterior intestinal portal. It eventually forms the central tendon of the diaphragm. Also contributing to the formation of the diaphragm are contributions from the body wall, the esophageal adventitia, and mesentery, and, as mentioned above, the pleuroperitoneal membranes.

D. Further subdivision of peritoneal cavity (Fig. 56)

1. *Greater sac* or *general peritoneal cavity*–This constitutes the bulk of the peritoneal cavity and is bounded therefore by the peritoneum lining the walls of the abdominal cavity and by its reflections upon the viscera except for a small area dorsal to the stomach which forms the:

2. *Lesser sac* (*omental bursa*)–This division of the peritoneal cavity is formed as rotation of the stomach occurs with simultaneous expansion of the dorsal mesogastrium to form the greater omentum, the ligaments (peritoneal reflections) which unite stomach and spleen, and spleen and dorsal body wall. (Fig. 56) The ventral mesogastrium also forms part of the wall of the lesser sac, with its free border forming the ventral boundary of the communication, the *epiploic foramen* (*foramen of Winslow*), between the two sacs.

III. Mesenteries

These have been partially considered with the development of the gut but a review of the derivatives of the primitive mesenteries will be presented here.

A. *Ventral mesentery* (Figs. 47,53,54,56)–It was noted above that the liver develops within the ventral mesogastrium and septum transversum. The umbilical vein also utilizes the ventral mesogastrium to pass through the liver as it courses to the heart.

1. *Falciform ligament*–This reflection of peritoneum is derived from that segment of the ventral mesogastrium between the liver and ventral body wall.

2. *Ligamentum teres*–This is the postnatal remnant of the obliterated umbilical vein which is found within the substance (between layers) of the falciform ligament.

3. *Coronary and triangular ligaments*–These ligaments are derived from the segment of the ventral mesentery between the liver and the septum transversum (later, the central tendon of the diaphragm).

4. *Lesser omentum*–This membrane is formed from that portion of the ventral mesogastrium which extends between stomach and liver. Due to the rotation of the stomach, this portion of the mesogastrium runs from its attachment to the stomach on the left to its free border on the right, i.e. in a frontal plane. It is subdivided into the:

a. *hepatogastric ligament*–This portion extends between the stomach and the liver.

b. *hepatoduodenal ligament*–This ligament is located between the liver and the duodenum.

B. Dorsal mesogastrium (Figs. 47,53,54,56)–This is the portion of the dorsal mesentery between the stomach and the dorsal body wall which contains the spleen and ultimately is divided into the:

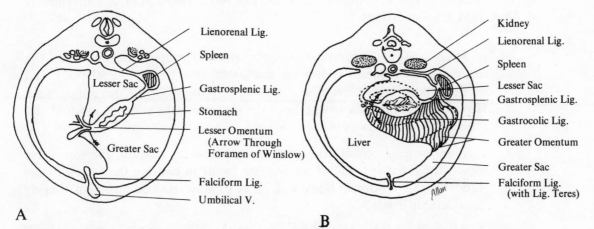

A   B

FIGURE 56. The peritoneal cavity. Cross sections of the embryo through the upper half of the peritoneal cavity. A. Beginning of rotation of stomach. B. Relationships in the definitive condition.

105

1. *Gastrolienal ligament* (*gastrosplenic*)–That portion of the mesogastrium between the stomach and spleen.

2. *Lienorenal ligament*–That portion of the mesogastrium between spleen and kidney on the dorsal body wall.

3. *Greater Omentum*–This is the greatly expanded portion of the dorsal mesogastrium which descends from the caudal portion of the greater curvature of the stomach then doubles back upon itself to ascend and attach to the dorsal body wall. It is therefore a double layer of mesentery. Since the greater omentum forms the floor of the lesser sac (omental bursa), a portion of the latter extends into or between these layers for a variable distance. As the greater omentum drapes over the intestine and colon, it frequently fuses to the transverse colon and forms the *gastrocolic ligament* between the stomach and colon. The lower part of the greater omentum appears therefore to arise from the transverse colon. (Figs. 47,56)

C. *Dorsal mesoduodenum*–As rotation of the stomach occurs, its pyloric region and the duodenum, including their dorsal mesentery, become fused to the dorsal body wall. (Fig. 47)

D. *Dorsal mesentery* (proper)–Unlike the duodenum, the remainder of the small intestine does not become fused to the dorsal body wall but remains suspended by its mesentery. Due to the extreme elongation of the gut and the corresponding growth of the side of the mesentery attached to it, the mesentery becomes shaped like a very broad fan. Its base is attached to the· dorsal body wall on an oblique line from the left of the midline cranially to the right of the midline more caudally. At this point the mesentery joins the mesocolon. (Figs. 47,52)

E. *Mesocolon*–The mesentery of the colon can be divided and more conveniently described in four portions:

1. *Mesocolon of the cecum* and *ascending colon*–The ascending colon and the cecum usually come in apposition with, then fuse to, the dorsal body wall on the right. Their mesocolon disappears by its fusion to the dorsal wall. However, the appendix arising from the cecum usually remains unfused and retains the small mesoappendix.

2. *Transverse mesocolon*–As noted in the preceding chapter, the transverse mesocolon is carried ventral to, and is a factor in causing the fusion of the duodenum to the dorsal body wall. It is usually retained although varying considerably in size.

3. *Mesocolon of the descending colon*–This segment of mesocolon becomes obliterated by its apposition to and fusion with the dorsal wall.

106

4. *Sigmoid mesocolon*–This is retained as a small mesentery which passes from the dorsal wall of the lower abdominal and pelvic cavities to the sigmoid colon.

5. *Mesorectum*–This is a transitory mesentery which is obliterated as the extension of the peritoneum on the rectum is reduced in its pelvic extent.

13

The Urinary System

I. Introduction

The bulk of this system is derived from the *nephrogenic tissue* of the intermediate mesoderm. This tissue gives rise to the *excretory portion* of the definitive urinary system, whereas the *collecting portion* of that system is derived from the endoderm of the primitive cloaca.

During embryological development the excretory organs seen in lower forms appear temporarily in the human embryo only to be replaced by the definitive kidney. Thus three kidneys appear during human embryonic life. Two of them, the *pronephros* and *mesonephros*, disappear and their ducts are retained and utilized by the reproductive system. The third and most complex is called the *metanephros*, which becomes the definitive kidney.

II. Pronephros (Figs. 57,58)

This organ appears as a series of paired buds which are derived from the *nephrotomes* (segmental structures derived from the nephrogenic cord). The following pronephric structures are formed from the nephrotomes and the buds:

A. *Pronephric tubules*–These tubules appear during the fourth week in segments 7-14 and communicate with the coelom via the:

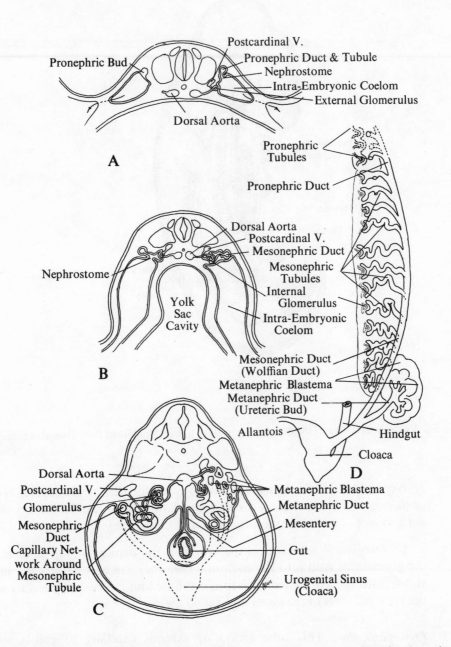

Pronephric Bud
Postcardinal V.
Pronephric Duct & Tubule
Nephrostome
Intra-Embryonic Coelom
External Glomerulus
Dorsal Aorta

A

Pronephric Tubules

Pronephric Duct

Dorsal Aorta
Postcardinal V.
Mesonephric Duct
Nephrostome
Mesonephric Tubules
Internal Glomerulus
Intra-Embryonic Coelom
Yolk Sac Cavity

B

Mesonephric Duct (Wolffian Duct)
Metanephric Blastema
Metanephric Duct (Ureteric Bud)
Allantois
Hindgut
Cloaca

D

Dorsal Aorta
Postcardinal V.
Glomerulus
Mesonephric Duct
Capillary Network Around Mesonephric Tubule
Metanephric Blastema
Metanephric Duct
Mesentery
Gut
Urogenital Sinus (Cloaca)

C

FIGURE **57.** Pronephros, mesonephros, and metanephros. A. Typical cross section of embryo through somites 7 to 14. Earlier stages of development on left. B. Typical cross section through somites containing mesonephros. Earlier stage of development on left. C. Typical cross section through caudal portion of the mesonephros and including part of the metanephros. Excretory ducts and cloaca outlined in dash line. D. Ventrolateral view of embryonic excretory system (schematic).

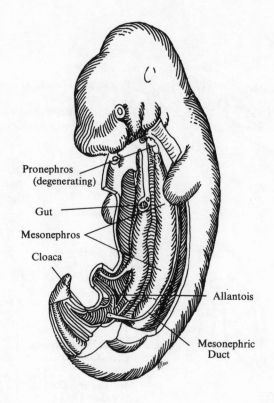

Pronephros
(degenerating)

Gut

Mesonephros

Cloaca

Allantois

Mesonephric
Duct

FIGURE **58.** Ventrolateral view of the dorsal body wall at 10 mm. (modified from several sources)

1. *Nephrostome*–This structure develops within the nephrotome. Near its coelomic end a structure develops consisting of a capillary loop covered with a layer of coelomic mesothelium; it is called the:

2. *Glomerulus*–Wastes within the blood in the capillary loop filter through the glomerular wall into the coelom where they are carried, via the nephrostome, into the associated pronephric tubule and collected by a duct joining the terminal ends of the latter and called the:

B. *Pronephric duct*–This tube grows or extends caudally to empty into the terminal portion of the hind gut, thus forming the cloaca. The more cephalic pronephric tubules, nephrostomes, and glomeruli are in the process of degeneration while the more caudal are being formed. The period in which this kidney can be observed is a short one.

110

III   Mesonephros (Figs. 57,58)

This organ is paired and is derived from nephrotomal tissue located just caudal (14-26th segments) to the pronephros. It appears during the fourth and fifth week of development. From the nephrotomes, noted above, buds appear which form the:

A. Mesonephric tubules–These tubules join the old pronephric duct as it extends caudally and by so doing convert it into the *mesonephric duct*. The mesonephric tubules differ from the pronephric tubules in that they lack a nephrostome, although the latter may appear transitorily, and have an:

1. *Internal glomerulus*–This glomerulus is formed as a capillary loop indents the blind end of a mesonephric tubule. Thus, wastes eliminated by the blood are passed into the tubule directly and then carried into the:

B. Mesonephric duct–This duct retains communication with the cloaca and serves as the collecting duct of the mesonephros.

The pronephros has little or no functional purpose in man. The mesonephros, however, is functional and continues to function for a while after the definitive kidney is formed. The mesonephros forms a longitudinal ridge on the dorsal wall of the coelom intimately associated with the genital ridge. It will be considered again in the next chapter because of that relationship.

IV.   The Metanephros or Definitive Kidney

This pair of organs is derived from primordia of two sources. The secretory portion is derived from the caudal end of the nephrogenic cord, here unsegmented, and the collecting or drainage portion of the organ is derived from an evagination of the mesonephric duct. This evagination is called the:

A. *Ureteric (metanephric) diverticulum* (Figs. 58,59,60)–From its origin, the diverticulum extends dorso-laterally and cephalad, where it meets the caudal portion of the nephrogenic cord. As this extension occurs, the duct undergoes repeated branching so that ultimately twelve generations of the branches are formed. The stem of the diverticulum becomes the:

1. *Ureter*–The stem dilates distally just prior to its primary branches and forms the:
2. *Renal pelvis*–The primary pair of branches arises from this dilation and becomes the:
3. *Major renal calyces*–The absorption of the tertiary and quaternary branches of the original diverticulum form subdivisions of the major calyces known as the:
4. *Minor renal calyces*–Tubules of the next (fifth) order of branches open into the minor calyces as:

111

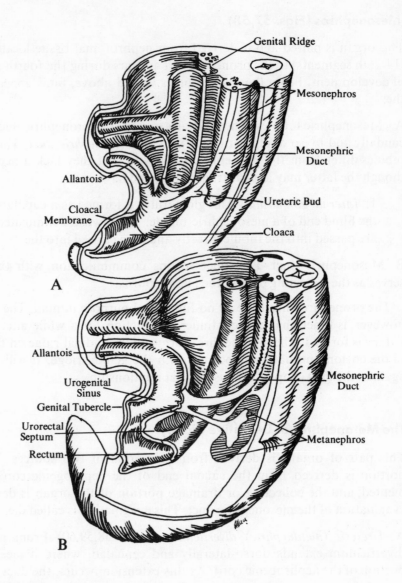

Genital Ridge

Mesonephros

Mesonephric
Duct

Allantois

Ureteric Bud

Cloacal
Membrane

Cloaca

A

Allantois

Mesonephric
Duct

Urogenital
Sinus

Genital Tubercle

Urorectal
Septum

Rectum

Metanephros

B

FIGURE **59.** Division of the cloaca (after Keibel and others) ventrolateral view.
A. At 5 mm. (32 days). B. At 13 mm. (40 days).

5. *Papillary ducts*-As the name implies, the ducts enter the calyces via papillae which project into the calyces and form the apex of the:

6. *Renal pyramid*-This is formed by many papillary ducts and their branches which also form the:

7. *Straight collecting tubules*-These tubules eventually unite with tubules formed by the nephrogenic tissue which is intimately related to the terminal ends of the ureteric diverticulum.

112

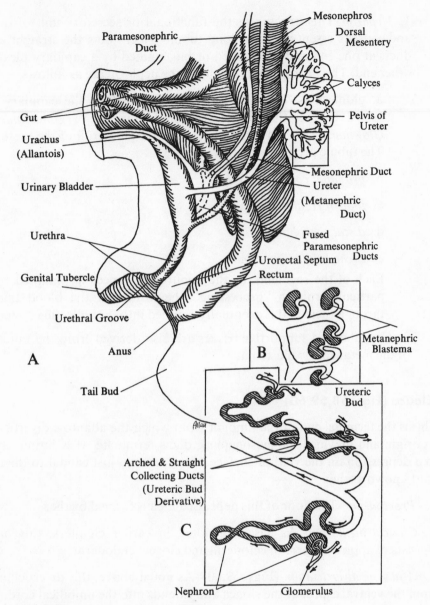

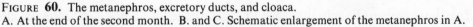

FIGURE **60.** The metanephros, excretory ducts, and cloaca.
A. At the end of the second month. B. and C. Schematic enlargement of the metanephros in A.

B. *Metanephric blastema* (Figs. 58,59,60)–As noted above, this tissue forms a cap on the ureteric diverticulum. With each division of the diverticulum there is a corresponding division of the blastemal cap, which covers each of the new divisions. Thus, when division or branching of the diverticulum is complete, a small mass of the blastemal tissue is in apposition to the terminal ends of the arched collecting tubules. This tissue differentiates into the tubules etc. of the excretory metanephros which constitute the:

113

1. *Nephron*–This structure is the functional or secretory unit of the kidney and consists essentially of a long tubule which joins the straight collecting ducts at one end and is indented or invaginated by a capillary plexus at the other end. The various components of the nephron are as follows:

a. glomerulus–This is the structure formed by the capillary loop invested with epithelium of the tubule forming a *glomerular capsule* (*Bowman's capsule*) and is comparable to glomeruli of the mesonephros. The tubule proper is divided into:

b. *proximal convoluted tubule*

c. *loop of Henle*

d. *distal convoluted tubule*

e. *arched collecting tubule*

Each of the segments of the nephron is especially adapted to play a particular role in "processing" the filtrate of the blood that passes through them and is eventually emptied into the collecting system.

2. Capsular and supportive tissues are also derived from the outer portion of the metanephric blastema.

V. Cloaca (Figs. 58,59,60)

This is the terminal end of the hindgut from which the allantoic diverticulum has its origin and in which the mesonephric ducts terminate. It is intimately related to a depression on the ventral surface of the embryo just caudal to the umbilical cord known as the:

A. *Proctodeum*–The floor of this depressed area is formed by the:

B. *Cloacal membrane*–As has been noted in earlier chapters, this membrane consists of apposed layers of ectoderm and cloacal endoderm.

C. *Allantoic diverticulum*–(Figs. 59,60)–As noted above, this diverticulum arises from the ventral aspect of the cloaca and extends into the umbilical cord.

D. *Urorectal septum*–Eventually, the cloaca is divided by a plate of tissue which grows caudally between its ventral (*urogenital sinus*) and dorsal (*rectum*) portions. The septum eventually reaches the cloacal membrane, thus completing the separation between rectum and the:

E. Urogenital sinus–The ventral portion of the cloaca expands somewhat and absorbs the proximal portion of the allantoic diverticulum and the terminal portions of the mesonephric ducts. In so doing, the proximal ends of the metanephric or ureteric ducts come to open into the sinus directly rather than by way of the mesonephric ducts. (Fig. 60) The sinus can now be divided into a ventral or:

114

1. *Pelvic portion* (Fig. 60)–The ureteric ducts open into this portion as does the allantoic diverticulum. This portion of the urogenital sinus will form the:

    a. *urinary bladder*–This organ is joined by the:

    b. *ureters*–These are derived from the ureteric or metanephric ducts.

    c. *urachus*–This structure is derived from the obliterated allantoic diverticulum.

2. *Urethral portion* (Fig. 60)–This portion of the sinus receives the mesonephric and the fused paramesonephric ducts. It becomes a part of the urethra in the male; the urethra and vestibule of the female. Details of the formation of the urethra can be presented better during consideration of the genital system and will be presented therefore in the next chapter.

14

Genital System

I. Introduction

Although the sex of the embryo is determined at the moment of union of sperm and ovum, it is not until toward the end of the second month that the sex is manifested in the genital organs. During the month preceding this manifestation, basic primordia are established which are common to both sexes. That is, the embryo undergoes an indifferent stage of development in which the anlagen of the genital organs of both sexes make their appearance. Later, the anlagen of one sex continue their development and differentiation, whereas the other set is converted into a group of vestigial structures.

II. Indifferent Stage

Certain of the ducts, ultimately becoming a part of the genital apparatus, originate as part of the urinary system of the early (7–10) somite embryo. Considerably later (4–5 mm. or late somite stage) the gonads are first observed and still later (15 mm. embryo) the external genitalia are established. A more detailed description of the anlagen appearing in both sexes follows:

A. *Internal genital organs* (Figs. 61,62)

1. *Gonads*–Primordia of the gonads appear in the 4 to 5 mm. embryo as ridges on the medial side of each of the mesonephroi. Cells comprising these primordia, which are called *genital ridges,* are derived from the mesothelium lining the coelom, its underlying mesenchyme, and the *primordial germ cells* which migrate into the primordium from the yolk sac endoderm. The genital ridges are coextensive with the intermediate two-thirds of the mesonephroi and, as the latter degenerate, the ridges are converted into the elongated gonads suspended from the dorsal body wall by the cranial and caudal ligaments of the degenerated mesonephroi. The caudal ligament anchors the gonad to the genital swelling and is called the *genito-inguinal ligament.* No sex differences are noticeable at this, i.e. about 15 mm., stage.

116

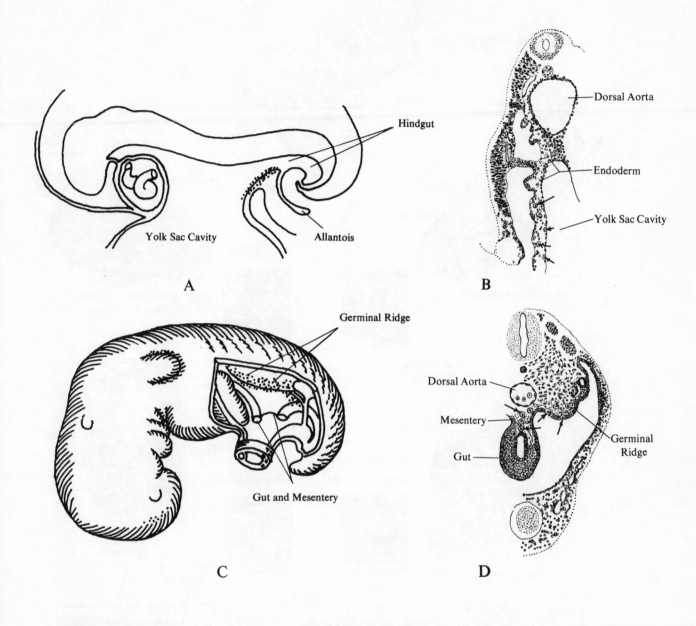

FIGURE **61.** Continuity of germ plasm.
A. A drawing of a 3 mm. embryo (25 days) with the location of the primordial germ cells indicated by black dots.
B. A drawing of the cross section of the same embryo showing the primordial germ cells as marked by arrows.
C. A drawing of an embryo at 4.2 mm. (30 days) showing primordial germ cells (black dots) migrating through the mesentery into the gonad.
D. A cross section of the embryo in C with primordial germ cells marked by arrows as they pass through the mesentery into the gonad. (Adapted from E. Witschi, '48. From *The Endocrinology of Reproduction* edited by J. T. Velardo, Oxford University Press, 1958.)

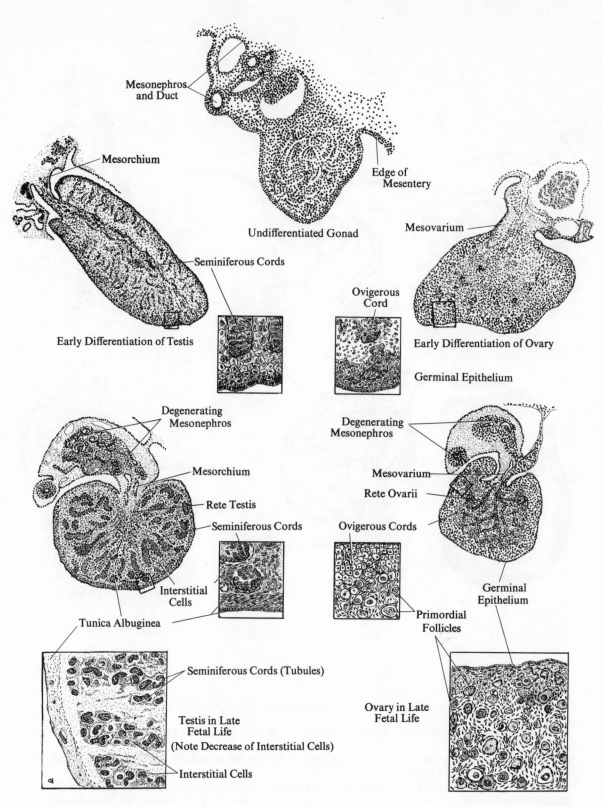

FIGURE **62.** Differentiation of the gonads.

118

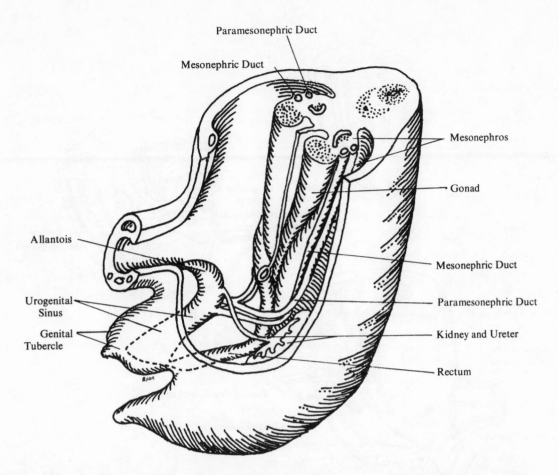

Paramesonephric Duct

Mesonephric Duct

Mesonephros

Gonad

Allantois

Mesonephric Duct

Paramesonephric Duct

Urogenital Sinus

Kidney and Ureter

Genital Tubercle

Rectum

FIGURE **63.** Genital ducts, undifferentiated stage. Drawing of a human embryo at about 15 mm. (42 days) with the upper half and left body wall cut away to demonstrate gonad, mesonephros and associated ducts, and urogenital sinus. The gut and its mesentery have also been removed. (modification from various sources including Hamilton, Boyd, and Mossman)

2. *Genital ducts* (Figs. 63,66,67)

a. mesonephric (*Wolffian*) ducts and associated mesonephric tubules– As noted in the previous chapter, these ducts served for the drainage of the mesonephric kidney. However, with degeneration of the latter the tubules are freed for possible use as segments of the definitive (particularly male) ducts. The ducts precede the gonad in development and are completely established, emptying into the cloaca, at the time the gonadal primordia are established.

FIGURE **62.** Differentiation of the gonads. This series of drawings represents the undifferentiated gonad (left) at the top and center. Differentiation into testis or ovary is represented on the left and right sides respectively. The drawings of the undifferentiated gonads represent stages occurring early, during the middle, and late in fetal life, from top to bottom, respectively. (drawing by Constance Herdeck. From *The Endocrinology of Reproduction* edited by J. T. Velardo, Oxford University Press, 1958.)

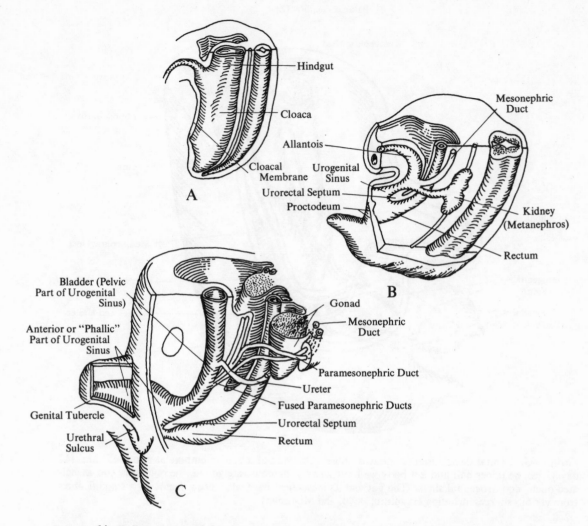

FIGURE **64.** Differentiation of the cloaca and urogenital sinus. The cloaca is indicated in A which is of the caudal end of an embryo at about 5 mm. (32 days). Separation of primitive urogenital sinus and primitive rectum is indicated (B) in an embryo of about 10 mm. (37 days). Further development of the embryo at 25 mm. (52 days) is represented at C.

b. *paramesonephric* (*Müllerian*) *ducts*–These ducts are first noted in the 10 mm. embryo lateral to the cranial end of the mesonephric duct. Each duct is laid down as a cord, which hollows out and extends caudally, eventually uniting in the midline with the duct from the opposite side. The fused caudal portion impinges on the posterior wall of the urogenital sinus, causing a swelling called the *Müllerian tubercle*.

B. External genitalia (Figs. 63,64,65)–The cloaca and later the urogenital sinus are located just internal to the site at which the external genitalia make their appearance. An intimate relationship exists, therefore, between these structures and a consideration of one necessitates a similar consideration of the

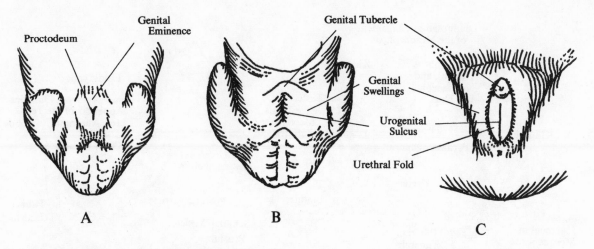

FIGURE **65.** External genitalia; undifferentiated stage. A, B, and C represent the primordia from which develop the external genitalia and are taken from five-, six-, and seven-week-old embryos respectively. (modified from several sources, especially Spaulding, '21)

other. The cloacal membrane, first observed in the embryonic disc stage, now lies on the ventral body wall. It is bounded laterally by the posterior limb buds, caudally by the tail or tail bud, and cranially by the umbilical cord. Several swellings are related to the cloacal membrane in this area. (Fig. 65) They are:

1. *Genital tubercle* (unpaired and midline)–This structure is located just ventral or cranial to the cloacal membrane.

2. *Genital swellings* (paired)–These structures are lateral to the tubercle and flank the:

3. Urethral folds (paired)–These folds bound the elongated *urethral groove* which is derived from the anterior part of the proctodeum.

After the division of the cloaca into the urogenital sinus and rectum is completed, the proctodeum is divided into a dorsal (anal) portion and a ventral (urogenital) portion. The similarly divided cloacal membrane degenerates, permitting communication between proctodeum and urogenital sinus ventrally and proctodeum and rectum dorsally. The genital swellings enlarge and the genital tubercle elongates. A plate of cells from the urogenital membrane extends into the genital tubercle along the mid-sagittal plane and forms the *urethral plate*. The latter is related externally to the urethral groove on the ventral surface of the genital tubercle. The urethral groove is continuous caudally with the *urogenital orifice*.

III. Differentiation

Modification of the anlagen or primordia of the genital system eventually occurs, thus establishing. the definitive genital system of one sex or the other. As noted above, this differentiation is largely due to genetic control. However,

121

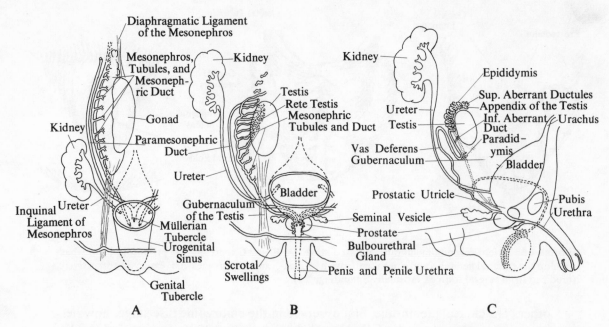

Diaphragmatic Ligament
of the Mesonephros

Mesonephros,
Tubules, and
Mesoneph-
ric Duct

Kidney

Gonad

Paramesonephric
Duct

Kidney

Ureter

Inquinal Ureter
Ligament of
Mesonephros

Müllerian
Tubercle
Urogenital
Sinus

Genital
Tubercle

Kidney

Testis
Rete Testis
Mesonephric
Tubules and Duct

Ureter

Bladder

Gubernaculum
of the Testis

Scrotal
Swellings

Penis and Penile Urethra

Kidney

Ureter

Testis

Vas Deferens
Gubernaculum

Prostatic Utricle

Seminal Vesicle

Prostate

Bulbourethral
Gland

Epididymis

Sup. Aberrant Ductules
Appendix of the Testis
Inf. Aberrant
Duct
Paradid-
ymis

Urachus

Bladder

Pubis
Urethra

A   B   C

FIGURE **66.** Genital ducts of the male. Diagrammatic representation of the differentiation of the male genital ducts. Undifferentiated stage (A); early differentiation (B); and the condition just prior to birth when testis is undescended (C). Dash lines indicate position of testis after descent and dotted lines the position of the obliterated paramesonephric duct. Vestigial structures retained from the latter are labeled. (From *The Endocrinology of Reproduction* edited by J. T. Velardo, Oxford University Press, 1958.)

it may be that the production of certain hormones by the differentiating gonad also plays a part in differentiation of the genital duct system and external genitalia.

A. Internal genital organs (Figs. 62,66)

1. *Testis*–At about the 14mm. stage histological differentiation of the gonad is initiated. Connective tissue septa appear and compartmentalize the testis. Between the septa the blastemal cells of the newly formed testis give rise to:

a. *seminiferous cords* (later *tubules*)–These cords include primordial germ cells. The cords converge on the hilum of the organ and form a network, the:

b. *rete testis*–This network becomes linked with the genital duct system by utilizing the mesonephric tubules (*efferent ductules*). The cords ultimately undergo canalization.

c. *interstitial cells*–These cells may be derived from the shorter segments of the seminiferous cord but are more likely derived from stromal mesenchyme.

The differentiation of the testis is very precocious when compared with that of the ovary.

122

2. *Internal descent of the testis* (Figs. 66,70)–A positional change of the testis occurs concomitant with the histological changes. As the mesonephros regresses, the testis assumes and utilizes its ligaments. The cranial (*suspensory*) ligament disappears whereas the caudal genito-inguinal (*gubernaculum testis*) ligament passes to the scrotal swelling and anchors the testis. Differential growth of the embryo causes the testis to shift caudally. That organ is within the pelvis by the end of the embryonic period.

3. *Ovary*–Histological differentiation of this organ is less well defined and lags behind that of the testis. Limited development of connective tissue permits proliferation of germinal cells from the surface epithelium at any time. The first growth of cells from the epithelium forms the: (Fig. 62)

    a. *primary cortex*–This consists of small clusters of cells among which are primordial germ cells. Later, the primary cortex is, in a sense, replaced by the:

    b. *secondary or definitive cortex*–This cortex is formed by elements of the primary cortex and a new proliferation from the germinal epithelium. The cortical material is broken up into ill-defined clusters of cells which form the:

        (1) *primordial follicles*–Each follicle contains a *primordial ovum* apparently derived from a primordial germ cell. Some of the primordial follicles become vesicular during late fetal life (probably due to the influence of maternal hormones) but then degenerate at birth.

        (2) *definitive follicles*–These follicles await the onset of puberty to develop as described in Chapter 1.

4. Positional change of the ovary–Like the testis, the ovary is retained or anchored to the labial swelling by the genito-inguinal ligament (later forming the *round ligament*) and descends into the pelvis due to differential growth of the posterior body wall. (Fig. 67)

5. Genital duct system

    a. *Male genital ducts* (Fig. 66)–Some of the primitive ducts are retained as part of the permanent duct system, others degenerate or become vestigial.

        (1) mesonephric tubules–The tubules which link the rete testis with the mesonephric duct are retained as the:
        (a) *efferent ducts*
        (b) *superior and inferior aberrant ductules*–These are derived from those tubules cranial and caudal, respectively, to the testis. The caudal group also gives rise to the *paradidymis*. They are vestigial and functionless.

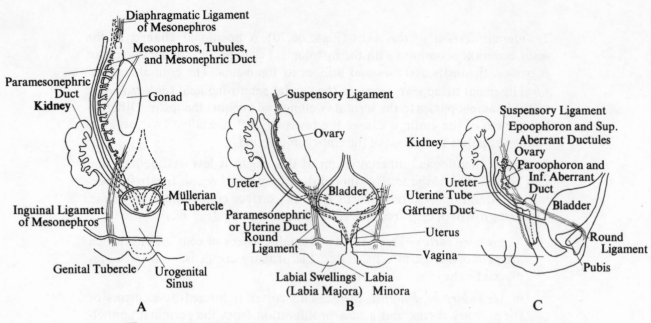

FIGURE 67. Genital ducts of the female. Diagrammatic representation of the differentiation of the female genital ducts. Undifferentiated stage (A); early differentiation (B); and the condition existing at birth (C). In the latter, the dotted lines indicate the position of the mesonephric duct and tubules. Vestigial structures derived from these are labeled. (From *The Endocrinology of Reproduction* edited by J. T. Velardo, Oxford University Press, 1958.)

(2) mesonephric (Wolffian duct)–This structure is retained to form the:

(a) *epididymidis*–This structure is derived from the cranial portion of the duct.

(b) *vas deferens*–This structure is derived from the major portion, especially the more caudal portion, of the duct.

(3) paramesonephric (Müllerian) duct–The cranialmost portion of the duct is retained as the:

(a) *appendix of the testis*–Whereas the:

(b) *prostatic utricle* (*utriculus masculinus*)–is derived from the terminal portion of the duct.

b. female duct system (Fig. 67)

(1) mesonephric tubules and duct–The cranial group of tubules and a segment of the duct form:

(a) *epoophoron* and *superior aberrant ductules*–These structures are retained as vestiges.

(b) *paroophoron* and *inferior aberrant ductules*–These structures are also vestigial and are derived from the lowermost portion of the mesonephric tubules.

(c) *Gartner's duct or canal*–This vestige represents the terminal end of the mesonephric duct.

124

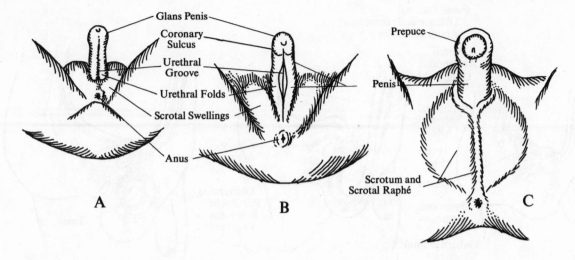

Glans Penis

Coronary
Sulcus

Urethral
Groove

Urethral Folds

Scrotal Swellings

Anus

Prepuce

Penis

Scrotum and
Scrotal Raphé

A   B   C

FIGURE **68.** Development of the external genitalia; differentiation of the male. A, B, and C represent the genitalia of fetuses of 8 weeks, 10 weeks, and near term. (modified from several sources, especially Spaulding, '21)

(2) paramesonephric or Müllerian duct–This duct forms virtually all of the definitive female ducts.

(a) *vesicular appendage*–This is a remnant of the cranialmost tip of the duct.

(b) *uterine tubes*–The bulk of each paramesonephric duct is retained as the respective uterine tube. Caudally the fused portions of the paired ducts form the:

(c) *uterovaginal tube*–The wall of this structure thickens and an indentation encircling the tube appears which marks the site of the *vaginal fornices*. The latter indicates the division of the tube into *uterus* and *vagina*. The *hymen* develops at the site of the Müllerian tubercle, i.e. at the junction of the paramesonephric duct (uterovaginal tube) with the urogenital sinus. It should be noted here that the genito-inguinal ligament, passing between the caudal end of the gonad and the labial swelling, becomes intimately associated with the lateral aspects of the uterus. This segment of the ligament becomes fibromuscular and, after fusion with the uterus, constitutes the round ligament of the uterus. It is, in part, homologous to the gubernaculum testis.

B. External genitalia

1. Male (Figs. 68,70)–Male characteristics of the genital tubercle, swellings, urethral folds and groove become apparent at the end of eight weeks.

a. genital tubercle–This structure elongates and, during the third month, develops a terminal swelling (*glans penis*) and later becomes the

125

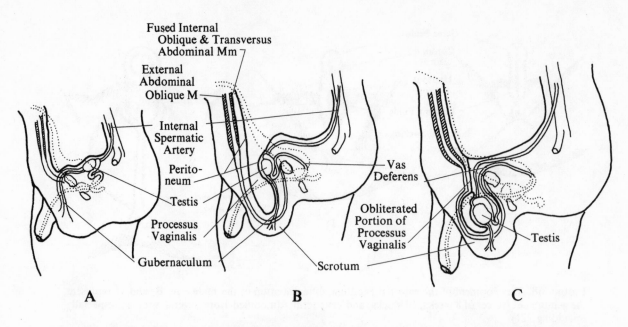

Fused Internal
Oblique & Transversus
Abdominal Mm

External
Abdominal
Oblique M

Internal
Spermatic
Artery

Peritoneum

Testis

Processus
Vaginalis

Gubernaculum

Vas
Deferens

Obliterated
Portion of
Processus
Vaginalis

Scrotum

Testis

A   B   C

FIGURE **69.** Descent of the testis. A, B, and C are parasagittal sections of the male fetus during the last trimester of intra-uterine life. The dotted lines represent the allantois or urachus, bladder, urethra, prostate and seminal vesicles, and the vas deferens which are in, or approach, the midline. (From *The Endocrinology of Reproduction* edited by J. T. Velardo, Oxford University Press, 1958.)

definitive *penis*. The *prepuce* develops as a ridge which grows distally to surround the glans to which it becomes fused. A secondary separation of prepuce and the glans occurs prior to birth.

b. urethral groove–The groove deepens and extends toward the tip of the tubercle where it meets a cord of cells (the urethral plate) which arose as an invagination from the tip of the glans. The cord is eventually canalized and is continuous with the *spongy* (*penile*) *urethra*. The latter is formed as the:

c. urethral folds approximate and fuse.

d. genital swellings–The swellings move caudally, enlarge, and become known as the *scrotal swellings*. They approach the midline and fuse, although the *scrotal raphé* and *septum* maintain separation. The scrotal swellings are converted into a sac, the *scrotum*, by the paired *vaginal processes* which are evaginations of the peritoneal cavity, carrying the rudimentary layers of the lower abdominal wall before them.

e. descent of the testis (Figs. 67,70)–The gubernaculum testis passes to the scrotal swelling via the posterior wall of the vaginal process and apparently participates in the descent of the testis from a position at the mouth of the process at the seventh month, to a position in the scrotum at term. The testis occasionally remains undescended at birth.

126

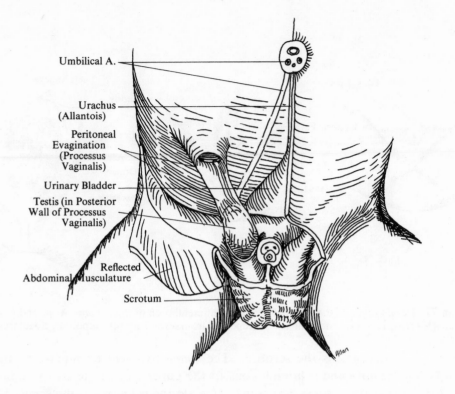

Umbilical A.

Urachus
(Allantois)

Peritoneal
Evagination
(Processus
Vaginalis)

Urinary Bladder

Testis (in Posterior
Wall of Processus
Vaginalis)

Reflected
Abdominal Musculature

Scrotum

FIGURE **70.** Descent of the testis. (after Kollman)

The communication of vaginal process with the peritoneal cavity is lost due to its obliteration by the fusion of its walls.

2. Female (Fig. 71)–The development of the female genitalia is generally protracted as compared to the male. The differentiation of the external genitalia into those which are recognizably female does not take place until the third month of development.

a. genital tubercle–This structure develops a caudal bend and becomes the *clitoris* which is, in part, the homolog of the penis. The development of a *glans clitoridis* and *prepuce* of the clitoris is similar and homologous to that in the male.

b. urethral groove–This groove is relatively short in the female.

c. urethral folds–These structures become plate-like and fail to fuse over the urethral groove. They become the *labia minora* and are homologous to the shaft of the male penis. The anterior part of the urogenital sinus and urethral groove are retained as the *vestibule* into which open both the urethra and vagina.

d. genital swellings–These elevations enlarge, become the labial swellings, and are ultimately converted into the *labia majora* whose male

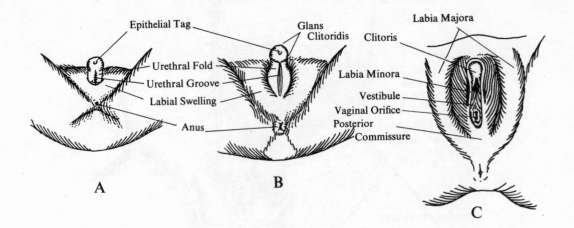

FIGURE **71.** Development of the external genitalia; differentiation of the female. A, B, and C represent fetuses of 9 weeks, 11 weeks, and near term. (modified from several sources, especially Spaulding, '21)

homolog is the scrotum. The *round ligament* terminates in the labia majora and is homologous to the gubernaculum testis. A rudimentary vaginal process occurs in the female and is known as the *canal of Nuck*.

C. Accessory organs of the genital system–These organs appear as epithelial outgrowths which are derived from segments of the urogenital tract.

1. Male–The organs are derived from the following segments of the male ducts: (Fig. 66)

a. vas deferens–Which gives rise to the:

(1) *seminal vesicle*–This organ appears near the caudal end of the mesonephric duct at its junction with the urogenital sinus. It begins its development at the end of the third month.

(2) *ejaculatory duct*–This duct is merely the specialized terminal portion of the vas deferens.

b. urethra (derived from urogenital sinus and urethral groove)

(1) *prostate*–At the end of the third month of development, this organ appears as a group of evaginations from the sinal portion of the urethra.

(2) *bulbo-urethral glands*–These glands also originate as an evagination of the sinal portion of the urethra.

(3) *urethral glands*–These small glands are derived from the urethral groove portion of the urethra.

128

2. Female–The accessory organs are less well defined as compared to the male but some homologs do appear. (Fig. 67)

    a. there are no homologs of the seminal vesicles or the ejaculatory duct

    b. vestibule and urethra (urogenital sinus)

        (1) *glands of Skene*–These glands are homologous to the prostate of the male and arise from the urethra.

        (2) *greater vestibular* (*Bartholin's*) *glands*–These are homologs of the bulbo-urethral glands of the male.

        (3) *lesser vestibular glands*–These are homologs of the urethral glands.

15

Skeletal and Muscular Systems

I. Skeletal System

The tissues comprising this system are derived from the mesoderm as condensations which may become ossified directly (*intramembraneous ossification*) or have a cartilaginous precursor which is later broken down and replaced with bone (*endochondral ossification*). The system consists of those elements, bone, cartilage, and fibrous tissue which form the framework of the body.

A. Axial skeleton (Figs. 21,72)–This portion of the skeleton is first represented by the notochord which is established in the late presomite and early somite embryo. It is soon (in the late somite embryo) replaced by the primitive vertebrae or the scleratomes which are derived from the somites. As development proceeds the axial skeleton becomes more complex and will be considered in more detail below:

 1. *Cranium* (skull)–Although a part of the axial skeleton, only a portion of the cranium is derived from the scleratomes. The greater portion of it is derived from the diffuse unsegmented mesenchyme of the head fold. (Fig. 73)

  a. *neurocranium*–This portion of the skull constitutes the brain case which is formed by some bones of intramembranous and others of endochondral origin.

   (1) *cartilaginous neurocranium*–This portion of the neurocranium is derived from the most cephalic somites, is the most ancient

phylogenetically, and forms the base of the neurocranium and capsules for certain (especially auditory and vestibular) sense organs. The following bones are ultimately derived from this source: *sphenoid*, *ethmoid*, part of the *occipital*, and the *petrous portion* of the *temporal bones*.

(2) *membranous neurocranium*–These bones develop in the outer layer of the meninges. They develop essentially for the protection of the larger and more specialized brain of man and the higher

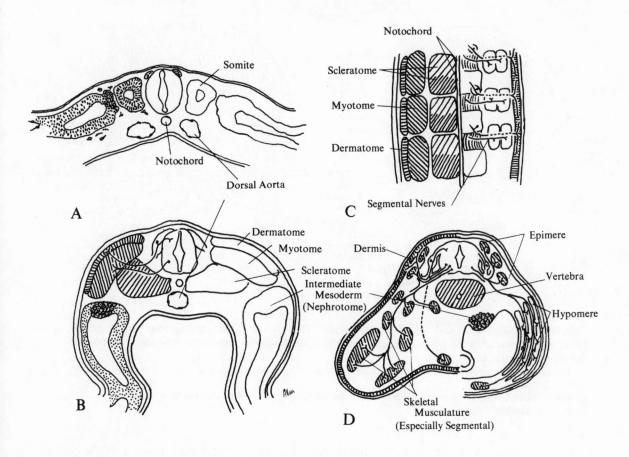

FIGURE **72.** Derivative of the somite, intermediate, and lateral plate mesoderm.
A. Typical cross section of an early somite embryo.
B. Typical cross section of the somite (Note cross-hatching, stippling, etc., and compare with C and D).
C. Schematic representation of somite derivatives from A and B above.
D. Typical cross section showing migration of muscle masses into limb (left) and body wall (especially on right).

131

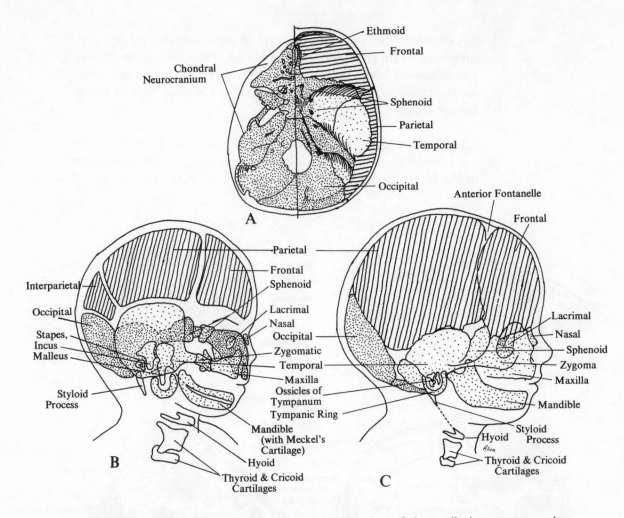

FIGURE **73.** The cranium and associated structures. Derivatives of the cartilaginous neurocranium, dense stipple; membraneous neurocranium, cross hatch; cartilaginous viscerocranium, clear; membraneous viscerocranium, open stipple.

A. The cranial floor from dorsal view. Left half representing fetus of three months, the right half the postnatal condition.

B. The cranium in lateral view (modified from Hamilton, Boyd, and Mossman) at three months.

C. Full term infant's cranium.

vertebrates and are therefore more recent bones from a phylogenetic standpoint. This recapitulation of the phylogenetic pattern is also paralleled by embryological development since the membranous neurocranium follows the cartilaginous neurocranium (which is seen in the seventh week) in its appearance. (Fig. 73) The following bones are part of the membranous neurocranium: *frontal* (paired), *parietal* (paired), part of the *occipital,* the *squamous portion* of the *temporal* (paired), *nasal* (paired), and *lacrimal* (paired).

132

b. *viscerocranium*–These bones constitute supportive elements of the face, i.e. those structures derived from the branchial arches. Here too are found bones of cartilaginous and membranous origin. The *cartilaginous viscerocranium* represents the skeleton of the primitive visceral or branchial arches whereas the *membranous viscerocranium* supplants or is added to the former. (Fig. 73)

   (1) cartilaginous viscerocranium–The bony elements derived from each of the arches are noted here:
      (a) first (mandibular) branchial arch–The skeleton of the first arch is called *Meckel's cartilage*, portions of which are retained as the *incus* and *malleus* of the middle ear and the *sphenomandibular ligament*. The bulk of Meckel's cartilage is replaced by the mandible, which is actually membranous bone.
      (b) second (hyoid) branchial arch–Portions of the cartilaginous skeleton of this arch (*Reichert's cartilage*) are retained as the *stapes, styloid process, stylohyoid ligament*, and the *lesser cornu* of the *hyoid bone*.
      (c) third branchial arch–The skeleton of this arch is retained as the *body* and *greater cornu* of the *hyoid bone*.
      (d) fourth, fifth, and sixth branchial arches–The *laryngeal cartilages* are derived from the skeletal elements of these arches.

2. Vertebral column (Figs. 72,74,75)–This structure forms around, indeed replaces, the notochord. Comprising it are the approximately 32 vertebrae, each of which is derived from a:

   (2) membranous viscerocranium
      (a) maxillary process–Simple mesenchymal condensations in this process give rise to the following bones: *maxilla, zygomatic, palatine, vomer.*
      (b) mandibular arch–As was noted above, the mandible replaces Meckel's cartilage and is formed as membraneous bone. In addition, this arch contributes to the tympanic plate or ring (around the tympanic membrane) which is a part of the temporal bone.

a. scleratome–This portion of the somite migrates medially and ventrally to surround the notochord. This is seen in the latter half of the fourth week of development. During the sixth week the scleratome becomes divided into a caudal half, whose tissues are more condensed, and a less condensed cranial half. The cranial and caudal portions become, respectively, the:

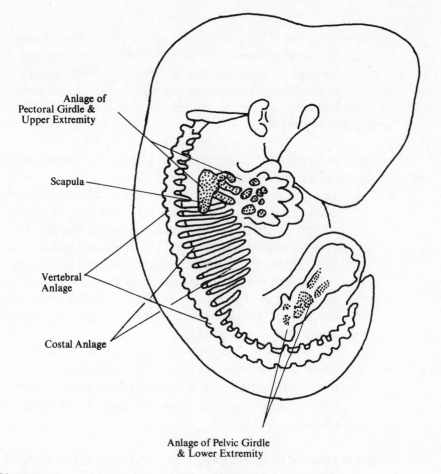

Anlage of
Pectoral Girdle &
Upper Extremity

Scapula

Vertebral
Anlage

Costal Anlage

Anlage of Pelvic Girdle
& Lower Extremity

FIGURE **74.** Skeletal system in an 11 mm. embryo (38 days). (after Bardeen)

(1) *intervertebral disc*–The remnant of the notochord can be identified as the center of the disc, which is called the *nucleus pulposus*.

(2) *vertebral bodies* and *processes*–These structures are derived from the cranial, less condensed, portion of the scleratome. They are first represented by cartilage which is transformed into bone.

3. *Ribs*–The ribs appear within the membranous body wall as areas of chondrification during the seventh week of development. They are apparently formed as *costal processes* of the scleratome. They appear associated with each of the vertebrae but fuse with the transverse process of the latter in all regions of the vertebral column except the thoracic, where they reach their maximum size.

4. *Sternum*–This structure appears in the sixth week as a pair of cartilaginous bars which connects the distal ends of the ribs with one another. The bars undergo a midline fusion in a craniocaudal direction.

134

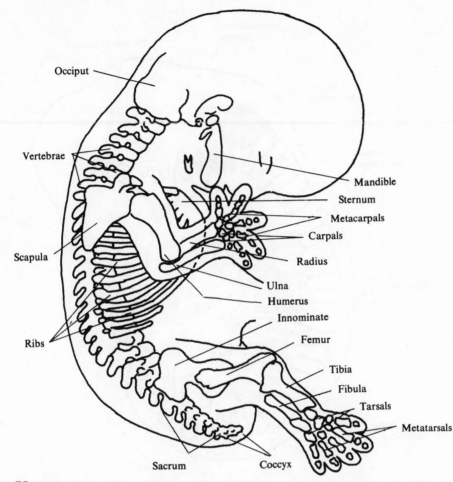

Occiput

Vertebrae

Scapula

Ribs

Mandible

Sternum

Metacarpals

Carpals

Radius

Ulna

Humerus

Innominate

Femur

Tibia

Fibula

Tarsals

Metatarsals

Sacrum

Coccyx

FIGURE **75.** Skeletal system in an 20 mm. embryo (47 days). (from several sources, including Bardeen)

The fusion is completed at nine months. Ossification begins in mid-fetal life.

B. *Appendicular skeleton* (Figs. 74,75)–The bones of the limbs appear as mesenchymal condensations (or *blastema*) within the limb bud during the fifth week. During the seventh week the blastema undergoes chondrification and at the eighth week ossification of the cartilaginous models of the larger bones is initiated. The appearance of blastema, chondrification, and ossification ot bones in the limbs occur essentially in a proximo-distal sequence. The anlagen of all of the bones are present when the embryo is at the 12 mm. (seventh week) stage. Ossification continues into postnatal life.

1. Pectoral girdle and bones of the upper extremity (Figs. 74,75)–These bones follow the general plan of development as noted in the preceding paragraph. However, the *clavicle* is an important variation. Unlike all other bones of the limbs, the clavicle is intramembranous in origin.

135

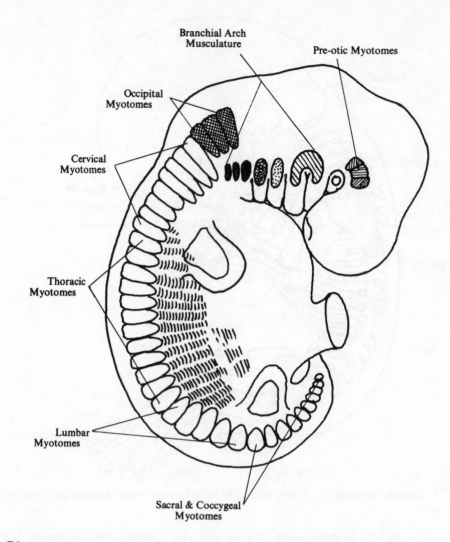

Branchial Arch
Musculature

Pre-otic Myotomes

Occipital
Myotomes

Cervical
Myotomes

Thoracic
Myotomes

Lumbar
Myotomes

Sacral & Coccygeal
Myotomes

FIGURE **76.** Schematic representation of the muscular system (myotomes) of an 8–9 mm. embryo (35–36 days). Note designation of branchial arch musculature and compare with Figures 77 and 78.

2. *Pelvic girdle* and bones of the *lower extremity*-Except for a slight lag in development as compared with the upper extremity, these bones follow the general plan of development noted above.

The primary centers of ossification are present at birth in most bones of each extremity with the exception of the carpal bones, the patella, and some of the tarsal bones.

C. *Joints*-The joints are derived from the mesenchyme between the potential articular surfaces of adjacent bones. In the more complex, synovial joints, a mesenchymal *joint disc* is established between the bones. The center of the disc degenerates to form a cavity which, as development proceeds, expands to cover the cartilaginous, articular surfaces of the bones.

136

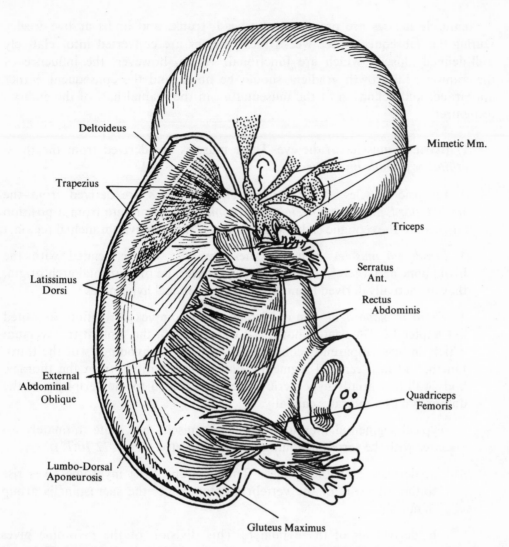

Deltoideus

Trapezius

Latissimus
Dorsi

External
Abdominal
Oblique

Lumbo-Dorsal
Aponeurosis

Mimetic Mm.

Triceps

Serratus
Ant.

Rectus
Abdominis

Quadriceps
Femoris

Gluteus Maximus

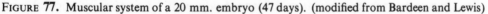

FIGURE **77.** Muscular system of a 20 mm. embryo (47 days). (modified from Bardeen and Lewis)

II. Muscular System

The tissues comprising this system are derived from mesoderm.

A. Segmented musculature (Figs. 72,76,77,78)–The bulk of skeletal or vol-
untary muscle is segmented and is derived from the myotome. The myotome is
derived from the somite and during the fifth week is divided into a dorsal
portion, the *epimere,* and a ventro-lateral portion, the *hypomere.* In some
instances the derivation of a particular muscle is not entirely clear, especially
in muscles of the extremities. Inclusion of such muscles as derivatives of
myotomes is based primarily on comparative studies and on a consideration of
the origin of the nerve fibers which constitute their innervation.

137

Premuscle masses are present in the head, trunk, and limbs at five weeks. During the subsequent three weeks these masses are converted into relatively well defined muscles which are functional. Again, however, the influence of the craniocaudal growth gradient should be noted and the consequent earlier appearance and definition of the musculature in the cranial half of the embryo recognized.

1. Extrinsic muscles of the eye–These muscles are derived from the three *orbital* or *pre-otic myotomes.*

2. Intrinsic muscles of the tongue–These muscles are derived from the *second, third,* and *fourth occipital myotomes* which migrate from a position adjacent to the cephalic end of the notochord into the hypobranchial region.

3. *Infrahyoid muscles*–Although these muscles are associated with the hyoid bone and, therefore, might be expected to be of branchial arch origin, they are actually derived from the first three cervical hypomeres.

4. *Thoracic diaphragm*–The diaphragm is of complex derivation, as noted in Chapter 12. The central portion is derived from the septum transversum which, in turn, apparently contains elements of the hypomeres of the third, fourth, and fifth cervical segments. Later, contributions from the thoracic body wall (essentially hypomeric muscle) are added to the periphery of the diaphragm as it migrates caudally.

5. Typical segmental musculature–These muscles are quite intimately associated with the vertebral column or axial skeleton. (Figs. 72,76,77)

   a. derivatives of the epimere–This portion of the myotome gives rise to the extensors of the vertebral column, i.e. the sacrospinalis group of muscles.

   b. derivatives of the hypomere–This division of the myotome gives rise to the musculature of the body wall, i.e. the intercostal and abdominal musculature. These are essentially flexors of the vertebral column. It should also be noted that the musculature of the ventral body wall (and the limbs) might be derived from or, at least, receive a contribution from the unsegmented lateral plate mesoderm.

6. *Pelvic diaphragm*–The muscles comprising this structure are derived from the third, fourth, and fifth sacral and first coccygeal hypomeres.

7. Musculature of the extremities–As noted earlier, the source of these muscles has not been clearly established. However, studies on their innervation and a comparison with lower forms suggest a myotomic origin. Within the extremity the muscles separate into a dorsal (extensor) group and a ventral (flexor) group. Each limb is also divided into a preaxial half and a postaxial half. (Figs. 72,76,77)

138

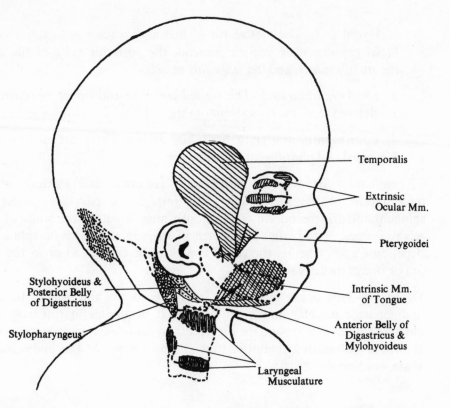

FIGURE **78.** Derivatives of branchiomeric musculature. Note designation of muscles derived from arches noted in Figure 76.

> a. upper extremities–The preaxial half of the upper extremities apparently receives contributions from the dermatomes, myotomes, and the corresponding nerves from cervical segments five, six, and seven. The postaxial half, on the other hand, has derivatives of the seventh and eighth cervical and first thoracic segments.
>
> b. lower extremities–The arrangement of the extensor and flexor groups of muscles is complicated in these extremities due to a rotation which has adapted them for the purpose of weight bearing. However, the preaxial half apparently receives segmental derivatives and nerves from the first through the fifth lumbar segments. The postaxial half receives similar contributions from the fifth lumbar and sacral segments one and two.

B. *Branchiomeric musculature*–These muscles are derived from the lateral plate mesoderm of the pharyngeal or branchial arches. (Figs. 76,78) Muscles derived from the various arches are listed below:

1. Mandibular arch–Mesoderm of this arch gives rise to the *muscles of mastication, the mylohyoideus,* the *anterior belly* of the *digastricus,* and the *tensors* of the *palate* and *tympanic membrane.*

139

2. Hyoid arch–The mesoderm of this arch gives rise to the *muscles of the facial expression* or *mimetic muscles*, the *posterior belly* of the *digastricus*, the *stylohyoideus*, and the *stapedius muscles*.

3. *Third branchial arch*–The *stylopharyngeus* and upper *pharyngeal muscles* are derived from the mesoderm of this arch.

4. Fourth, fifth, and sixth branchial arches–These arches give rise to the laryngeal and pharyngeal musculature.

C. *Involuntary* or *visceral musculature* (smooth and cardiac muscle)–The musculature of the heart, gut, and respiratory passages is derived from splanchnopleuric mesoderm. The smooth muscle within the walls of blood vessels is formed *in situ* from mesoderm of the somatopleure or splanchnopleure, depending upon whether the vessel is within the body wall or in the wall of the gut or one of its derivatives.

D. *Fascia*–This tissue is derived from mesoderm and serves to encapsulate and separate muscles and other organs. It originates *in situ* from the mesenchyme between and around the primordia of muscles, bones, vessels, and viscera. It should be realized therefore that all the fasciae of the body are, in a real sense, continuous.

16

Central Nervous System

I. Introduction

The central nervous system is composed of the brain and spinal cord and is derived from the *neurectoderm*. The latter first appears in the late presomite embryo as the thickened *neural plate* overlying the notochordal process. As the latter process extends caudally, differentiation of the overlying ectoderm into the neural plate takes place concomitantly. It is from this plate of tissue that all portions of the central nervous system have their origin. The covering (*meninges*) of the central nervous system develops *in situ* from the mesenchyme which surrounds the neural tube.

II. Formation and Differentiation of Neural Tube

At the beginning of somite formation the neural plate extends from the edge of the prochordal plate to the caudal edge of the embryonic disc. In this position it lies over the notochord and medial edge of the somites. A groove appears in the midline of the plate and its edges become elevated. The groove and elevations which flank it become, respectively, the:

141

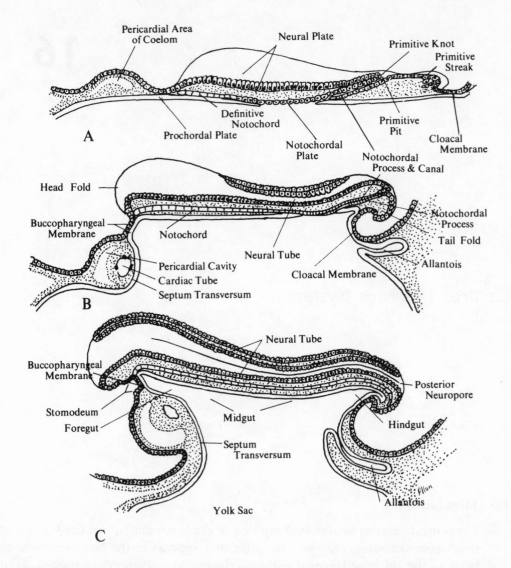

FIGURE **79.** The embryo during the fourth (and fifth) week of development (midsagittal sections). A. At beginning of somite formation. B. Early somite embryo. C. Late somite embryo (early in fifth week).

A. *Neural groove* and *neural folds* (Figs. 79,80)–The neural folds become increasingly prominent, especially at the cephalic end, as development proceeds. A secondary groove appears bilaterally in the cephalic portion of the fold and is called the *optic sulcus*. The latter is converted into the primordium of a major portion of the definitive eye.

As the neural groove deepens, the lateral extremities of the neural folds become elevated considerably and approach each other in the midline. The extremities eventually meet and fuse dorsally in the region of the fourth somite (in a seven somite embryo), thus forming the:

142

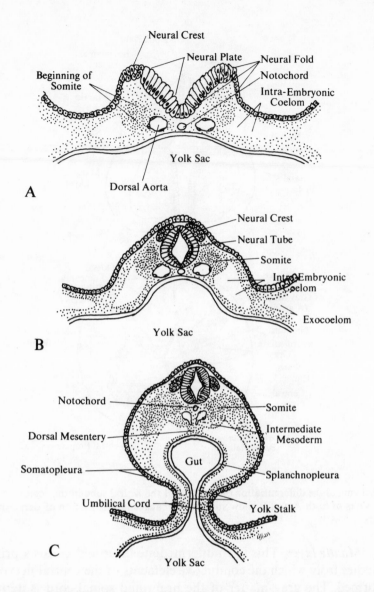

FIGURE **80.** The embryo during the fourth (and fifth) week of development (cross section). At beginning of somite formation (see Fig. 21A). B. Early somite embryo (see Fig. 21B). C. Late somite embryo (see Fig. 21C).

B. *Neural tube* (Figs. 79,81,82,83)–Elongation of the tube occurs as fusion of the neural folds continues cephalically and caudally. The cavity of the tube is the primitive *neural canal*. The latter opens at its extremities via the *anterior* (*cephalic*) and *posterior* (*caudal*) *neuropores* which are closed in the twenty somite stage when the fusion of the neural folds is completed.

Late in the fourth week the central nervous system is represented by walls of the neural tube which then undergo a histological differentiation resulting in the establishment of the following layers: (Figs. 81,82)

1. *Ependymal layer*–This is the innermost layer which is destined to become the supportive, non-nervous elements of the central nervous system.

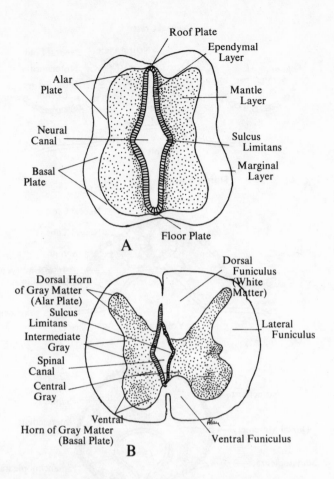

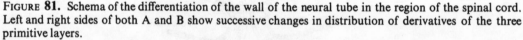

FIGURE **81.** Schema of the differentiation of the wall of the neural tube in the region of the spinal cord. Left and right sides of both A and B show successive changes in distribution of derivatives of the three primitive layers.

2. *Mantle layer*–This is an intermediate layer and consists primarily of cell bodies from which the conductive elements of the central nervous system are formed. The gray matter of the brain and spinal cord is derived from this layer. In certain segments of the brain migration of cells from this layer to the surface of the tube gives rise to the *cortex* (*cerebral, cerebellar*).

3. *Marginal layer*–This is the outermost layer of the tube and consists principally of the processes of nerve cells which comprise the white matter of the central nervous system.

C. *Neural crest* (Figs. 80,88)–These structures are derived from tissue associated with the lateral margin of the neural plates. As the neural folds raise and fuse in the midline, the neural crest tissue is carried into a position dorsolateral to the neural tube. With differentiation it becomes the source of neural elements of the *spinal ganglia* and, perhaps, of *sympathetic ganglia* as well. In addition, the *neurolemma* (*Schwann cells*) which are supportive tissue elements of peripheral nerves have origin from this tissue.

144

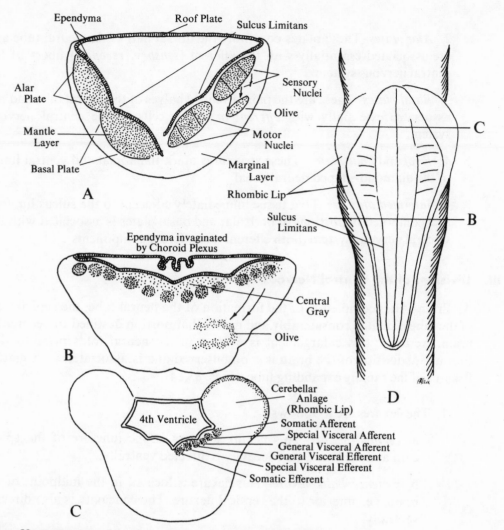

FIGURE 82. Derivatives of the alar and basal plates in the brain stem.
A. Progressive stages of differentiation in myelencephalon (earlier stage of development on left) in cross section.
B. Later stage of development of myelencephalon showing afferent and efferent cell columns (see C for labels of the latter) in cross section.
C. The metencephalon in cross section.
D. Dorsal view of neural tube noting position at which sections B and C were taken.

D. Structural differentiation of the neural tube (Figs. 81,82)–As will be shown later in this chapter the morphologic division described below has certain important functional connotations. In general, structures derived from the dorsal half of the neural tube give rise to sensory or receptive elements. On the other hand, those structures derived from the ventral half of the neural tube are essentially motor in nature.

1. *Sulcus limitans*–This is a groove which appears on the inner wall of the neural tube which divides the latter into dorsal and ventral halves.

145

2. *Alar plates*–These plates constitute the dorsal half of the neural tube and are associated essentially with the afferent (*sensory, receptor*) fibers of the central nervous system.

3. *Basal plates*–These are the paired ventral halves of the neural tube and are associated essentially with *efferent* or *motor* cells of the central nervous system.

4. *Roof* and *floor plates*–These structures mark the dorsal and ventral limits of the diamond-shaped neural canal.

5. *Intermediate zone*–That tissue immediately adjacent to the sulcus limitans and composed of portions of both alar and basal plates is associated with the visceral nervous system (both efferent and afferent components).

III. Divisions of the Central Nervous System

A. Brain–After completion of the formation of the neural tube, the cephalic end of the tube is dilated considerably and marks that portion destined to become the brain. Actually, this enlargement is evident in the neural folds prior to their fusion. Subdivision of the brain is soon observed and is associated with marked flexures of the rapidly expanding tube. (Figs. 83,84)

1. The flexures are as follows:

a. *cervical flexure*–This flexure appears at the juncture of the spinal cord and the brain. Its concavity is directed ventrally.

b. *mesencephalic flexure*–This flexure is located in the midpoint of the brain, i.e. anterior to the cervical flexure. The concavity is also directed ventrally.

c. *pontine flexure*–The third flexure occurs midway between the previously mentioned flexures. However, its concavity is directed dorsally.

d. *telencephalic flexure*–Growth of the telencephalon (part of the primitive *forebrain*) in a dorsocaudal direction results in this flexure.

2. Divisions of the brain (Figs. 83,84)–The primitive segments of the brain appear as three expansions of the tube which are described below:

a. *prosencephalon* (forebrain)–This is the most cranial of the brain vesicles and is limited cranially by the *lamina terminalis*. The prosencephalon is divided into the following:

(1) *telencephalon* (*cerebral hemisphere*)–These vesicles arise as paired lateral evaginations from the cranial end of the forebrain. The lamina terminalis is retained as a series of commissures or communications between the cerebral hemispheres. The *corpus callosum*

146

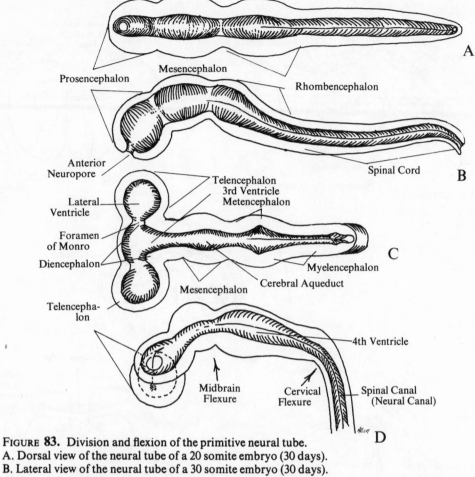

FIGURE **83.** Division and flexion of the primitive neural tube.
A. Dorsal view of the neural tube of a 20 somite embryo (30 days).
B. Lateral view of the neural tube of a 30 somite embryo (30 days).
C. Dorsal view of the neural tube in a 10 mm. embryo (37 days).
D. Dorsal view of the neural tube in a 10 mm. embryo (37 days).

and *anterior commissure* are two such derivatives of the lamina terminalis.

(2) *diencephalon*–This structure is derived from that portion of the forebrain behind the telencephalic evaginations. *Optic primordia* the *infundibulum,* and the *posterior lobe* of the *hypophysis* have origin from this segment as does the *thalamus* and its subdivisions (*dorsal thalamus, epithalamus, hypothalamus, metathalamus, subthalamus*).

b. *mesencephalon* (*midbrain*)–This is the middle primitive brain segment and is retained *in toto* as the midbrain of the adult. It can be divided into the dorsal *tectum* (essentially alar plate), a ventral *tegmentum* (essentially basal plate), and the *basic* (*cerebral*) *peduncles* all of which extend into the prosencephalon.

147

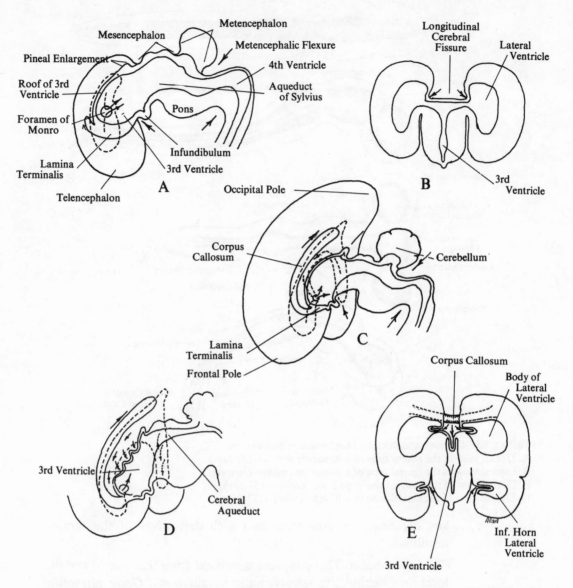

FIGURE **84.** Schematic representation of changes in the brain. (Dash-line in A, C, and D indicates position of lateral ventricle) A, C, and D. Midsagittal sections, B and E. Frontal sections. Note arrows indicating points at which invagination of tela choroidea forms the choroid plexuses.

c. *rhombencephalon* (*hindbrain*)–This is the terminal primitive brain segment, which is continuous caudally with the spinal cord. It is further divided into the:

(1) *metencephalon*–This portion of the hindbrain is continuous cranially with the midbrain. The dorsal portion of the tube (alar plate) undergoes an enlargement to form the *cerebellum*. The basal

148

plate of the metencephalon forms the *tegmentum* of the *pons*. The latter is formed in conjunction with the cerebellum.

(2) *myelencephalon*–This is the caudal portion of the rhombencephalon which becomes the *medulla oblongata*. Its basic structure is similar to that of the spinal cord. However, expansion of the roof plate and divergence of the alar plates result in a flattening out of this segment of the neural tube. This results in the formation of a rhomboid-shaped cavity from the neural canal. The sulcus limitans is still evident bilaterally in the floor of the rhomboid fossa and separates the now medial basal plate from the now lateral alar plate. (Fig. 82) Following the pattern noted above, the motor nucei can be found medial to the sulcus limitans whereas the sensory nuclei are located lateral to the sulcus.

B. Spinal cord (Figs. 81,83)–The spinal cord retains much of the primitive structure of the neural tube. The mantle layer becomes the gray matter of the cord and is located around the ependyma of the *central canal* or remnant of the lumen of the neural tube in this region. In cross section the gray matter has the shape of a butterfly. The dorsal half of the gray matter makes up the paired *dorsal columns* whereas the ventral half becomes the corresponding ventral gray columns. The marginal layer becomes the white matter which is divided into the four *funiculi*. It is utilized by fibers which ascend or descend within the central nervous system.

IV. Cavities of the Central Nervous System

These cavities are all derived from the primitive neural canal which is the interval or space between the walls of the neural tube. As noted earlier in this chapter, the canal is, at first, open cranially and caudally via the cranial and caudal neuropores. However, with their occlusion it becomes a sealed cavity. Expansion and modification of the canal parallels the differentiation of the various segments of the brain. (Figs. 83,84,85)

A. Canal of the prosencephalon

1. *Lateral ventricles*–These cavities arise with the telencephalic hemispheres as bilateral evaginations of the prosencephalic canal. They extend into the several expansions of the telencephalon and form, thereby, the *anterior, inferior,* and *posterior horns* (*cornua*) and *body* of the lateral ventricle.

2. *Third ventricle*–This is derived from the cavity of the diencephalon (caudal prosencephalon) and communicates with the lateral ventricles via the *interventricular foramina* (*foramina of Monro*) located at the site where evagination of the telencephalon occurred. Caudally, the third ventricle is continuous with the:

149

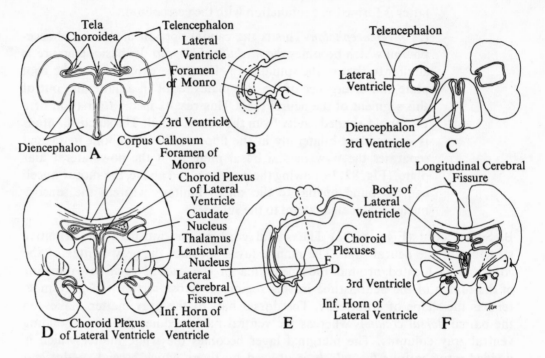

FIGURE 85. Relations of the derivatives of the telencephalon and diencephalon. A and C. Cross sections through brain as indicated on B, which is a midsagittal view. D and F. Cross sections (at a later developmental stage) through brain as indicated on E, which is a midsagittal view of the brain.

3. *Mesencephalic canal*–This segment of the primitive canal is reduced relatively in size by growth of the wall of the tube. It is retained as the *cerebral aqueduct* (*aqueduct of Sylvius*). It is continuous caudally with the:

B. *Rhombencephalic cavity*–This cavity is rhomboidal or diamond-shaped, as has been noted above. Its acute angles are directed cranially and caudally. At these extremities it communicates with the cerebral aqueduct and the *spinal canal* respectively and is called the *fourth ventricle*. The expanded dorsal portion of the metencephalon and the roof plate of the myelencephalon form the roof of the ventricle. The floor is formed by the tegmentum of the metencephalon and the medulla oblongata. It is continuous caudally with the:

C. Canal of the spinal cord (central canal) (Figs. 81,83)–This canal is much reduced in size as compared with other derivatives of the neural canal and so remains in the definitive condition.

D. *Choroid plexuses* (Figs. 84,85)–During development certain portions of the wall of the neural tube become greatly reduced in thickness. Indeed, this reduction continues until only the innermost layer (ependyma) of the neural tube

150

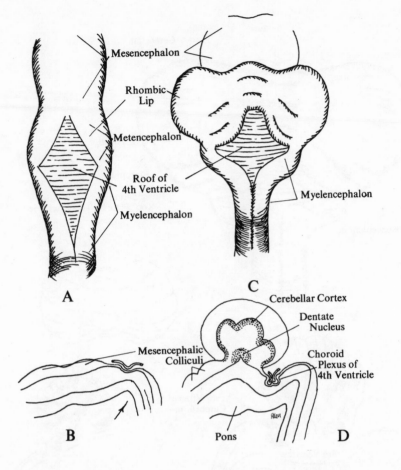

FIGURE **86.** Development of the metencephalon (cerebellum). A and B. Dorsal and midsagittal views respectively of the early metencephalon and myelencephalon. C and D. Dorsal and midsagittal views respectively of the same area at a later stage of development. Note the expansion of the rhombic lip to form the cerebellum.

remains. This process is apparent particularly in the medial wall of the telencephalic hemispheres, the roof of the diencephalon, and the expanded roof of the myelencephalon. Vascular tufts of the pia mater (*tela choroidea*) invaginate the thin walls, at the points noted above, carrying the ependyma before them. In this manner the choroid plexuses of the various ventricles are formed. Thus, such plexuses are found in both lateral ventricles and in the roofs of the third and fourth ventricles.

The ventricular system contains the *cerebrospinal fluid* which is produced within the system, at least in part, by the choroid plexuses. The fluid escapes the system and enters the *subarachnoid space* (between the meninges) via foramina in the roof of the fourth ventricle.

151

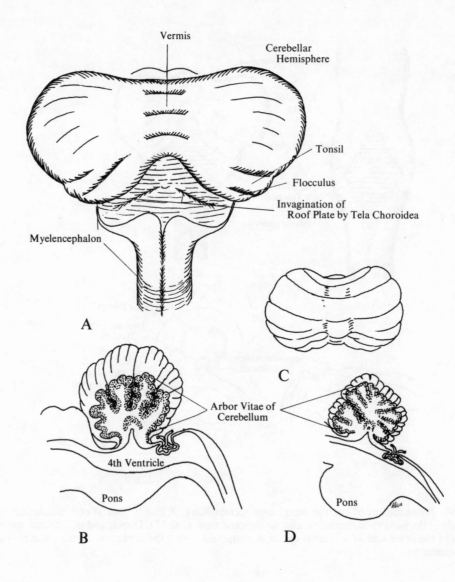

Vermis

Cerebellar
Hemisphere

Tonsil

Flocculus

Invagination of
Roof Plate by Tela Choroidea

Myelencephalon

A

C

Arbor Vitae of
Cerebellum

4th Ventricle

Pons

B

Pons

D

FIGURE 87. Later stages in the development of the cerebellum. A and C. Dorsal views. B and D. Mid-sagittal views.

V.   External Changes in the Neural Tube (Figs. 83,84,85,86,87)

As noted above, the neural tube is markedly expanded at its cranial end in such a manner that the primitive segments, hence external configuration, are easily observed. In addition, the cervical, mesencephalic, pontine, and telencephalic flexures have been considered. As development proceeds and expansion of the brain vesicles occurs, the flexures become exaggerated, then erased somewhat by the fusion of their contiguous surfaces.

152

A. Cerebral hemispheres (telencephalic vesicles) (Figs. 84,85)–The changes which occur in these vesicles overshadow other less extensive changes in the cranial end of the neural tube. Thus, the hemispheres expand cranially, dorsally, and caudally from the point of original evagination from the prosencephalon. These expansions give rise to the following:

1. *Frontal lobes*–These are formed by the cranial growth or extension of the hemispheres. On their ventral aspects appear the *olfactory bulbs*.

2. *Parietal (lobes) areas*–These are formed by the dorsal and part of the caudal expansions of the vesicles.

3. *Insula (island of Reil)*–The ventral and lateral aspects of the hemispheres become depressed by the more rapid growth of adjacent portions of the vesicles. As these portions overlap the depressed portion (insula) they form the *lateral cerebral fissure (Sylvian fissure)*.

4. *Temporal lobes*–These arise just caudal to the insula and grow ventrally and cranially to lie over the insula and form the ventral border of the lateral cerebral fissure.

5. *Occipital lobes*–These lobes are derived from the posterior extremity of the telencephalic expansion.

B. Diencephalon–The growth of this segment does not match that of the telencephalon and as a result it is retained as a relatively simple structure which is overlapped by the cerebral hemispheres.

C. Mesencephalon–This segment also fails to undergo growth comparable to other portions and is therefore retained as a relatively small segment between the medial aspects of the cerebral hemispheres at their caudal poles.

D. Metencephalon (Figs. 86,87)–A considerable dorso-lateral expansion of the alar plates of the metencephalon gives rise to the primordia of the cerebellum which fuse in the midline. Near the midline, bilateral swellings fuse and form the *vermis*. More laterally, the edge of the alar plate (*rhombic lip*) forms the *flocullus* and *nodulus*. The bulk of the expansion forms the *cerebellar hemispheres* which become increasingly convoluted by the more rapid proliferation of the cells in the outer (cortical) layer of the hemispheres.

The tegmentum of the metencephalon becomes covered on its ventral surface by the pons which consists of fibers passing between nuclei of the tegmentum and the newly developed cerebellum.

E. Myelencephalon–This segment retains the basic, primitive structure of the neural tube with the exception noted above. One structure which is apparent externally is the *olive*, which is seen bilaterally on the ventro-lateral aspect of the medulla. The olives are derived from the alar plate and migrate to the position noted above.

VI. Meninges

The mesenchyme which surrounds the developing neural tube becomes specialized and is retained as the meninges of the central nervous system. In several situations these tissues are particularly modified and worthy of special note. As the cerebral hemispheres expand dorsally and toward the midline, they trap some of the mesenchymal tissue between them. This becomes the:

A. *Falx cerebri*-This structure is retained and occupies the *longitudinal cerebral fissure*. Within it develop some of the major venous sinuses which drain the brain.

B. *Tentorium cerebelli*-This structure has an origin similar to that of the falx cerebri, but is located between the occipital lobes of the cerebrum and the cerebellum, i.e. within the transverse cerebral fissure.

C. Choroid plexuses-As noted above, these are formed by an invagination of the tela choroidea and ependyma into the several ventricles of the brain. The pia mater which forms the vascular tuft or tela choroidea is located in the transverse cerebral fissure and extends laterally from that position into the lateral ventricles and ventrally into the roof of the third ventricle. Similar tissue is located between the cerebellum and roof of the fourth ventricle. Again, it should be noted that these plexuses are a source of the cerebrospinal fluid.

154

17

Peripheral Nervous System, Sympatho-Chromaffin

System, Prenatal Function of the Nervous System

I. Introduction

The peripheral nervous system includes all those nerves that proceed from the central nervous system and extend to the various tissues and organs of the body. The fibers that comprise these nerves are derived from cell bodies within the central nervous system or from cells of the neural crest, as was indicated in the last chapter. The neurolemma of the peripheral nerves also has origin from the neural crest. Other connective tissue elements of the peripheral nerve (*endoneurium*, *epineurium*, and *perineurium*) are derived from the mesenchyme associated with the fiber in the peripheral tissues.

II. Craniospinal Nerves

This division of the peripheral nervous system includes those nerves which arise directly from the brain or spinal cord. Various types of nerve fibers may be found in these nerves. However, all types of fibers are not necessarily found in each nerve. The distribution of the nerve or its branches determines the type of fiber to be found therein.

A. Nerve fiber components (Figs. 88,89)–The origin and distribution of the various types of nerve fibers are listed below:

1. Basal plate–Cells in the mantle layer of this plate give rise to fibers which will ultimately carry impulses (efferent) away from the central nervous system. Depending upon the origin of the tissues effected by stimuli passing via these fibers, the following types of efferent fibers can be described:

a. *somatic efferent*–These fibers pass to the muscles derived from the somites.

b. *special visceral efferent*–Fibers of this type pass to muscles which are derived from branchial arch mesoderm.

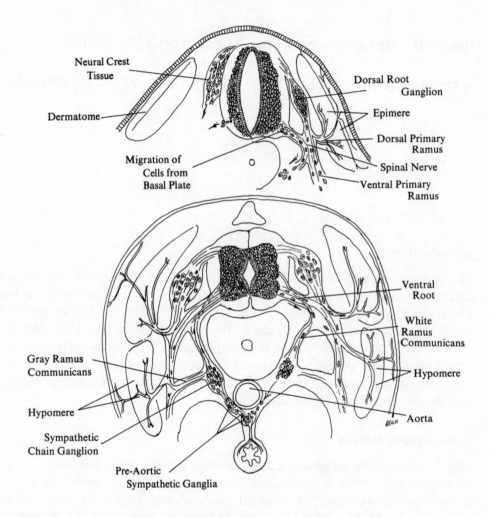

FIGURE **88.** Stage in the extension of the peripheral nerves (including sympathetic elements) into the tissue of the developing embryo.

156

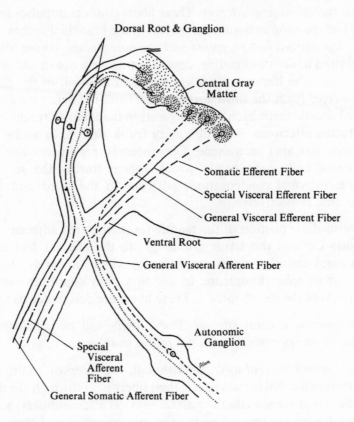

Dorsal Root & Ganglion

Central Gray
Matter

Somatic Efferent Fiber

Special Visceral Efferent Fiber

General Visceral Efferent Fiber

Ventral Root

General Visceral Afferent Fiber

Autonomic
Ganglion

Special
Visceral
Afferent
Fiber

General Somatic Afferent Fiber

FIGURE 89. Components of the peripheral nerves.

2. Alar plate and neural crest–Bipolar, cells which are derived from the neural crest form segmental cellular aggregates, the *spinal ganglia,* associated with the dorsal root of each spinal nerve. The bipolar cell sends one of its processes into the peripheral tissues and the other into the alar plate where it establishes connections with the cells located there. The peripheral process forms one of several possible end organs which are sensitive to a particular stimulus. Again, depending upon the type of tissues in which the receptors or end organs are to be found, several types of fibers are distinguishable which conduct impulses (afferent) from the receptor into the central nervous system.

a. *general somatic afferent*–The receptor endings of these fibers develop in tissues derived from the somatopleure.

b. *special somatic afferent*–These fibers have specialized receptors which develop in association with the somatopleure of the head, more particularly the otocyst.

157

c. *special visceral afferent*-These fibers conduct impulses from receptors which develop in tissues derived from the branchial arches.

Specialized *baroreceptors* and *chemoreceptors,* whose fibers would be classed under this heading, develop intimately associated with the aortic arches. The baroreceptors are found in the wall of the carotid sinuses (derived from the third aortic arches) and the definitive aortic arch (the left fourth aortic arch). The suggestion that similar receptors exist in the ductus arteriosus and pulmonary trunk (left sixth aortic arch derivatives) has also been made. Chemoreceptor elements are found in the *carotid* and *aortic bodies* which appear during the seventh week as mesenchymal condensations adjacent to the third and fourth aortic arches, respectively.

3. Intermediate portion of the mantle layer (the area adjacent to the sulcus limitans)-Cells of this tissue give origin to the efferent and afferent fibers (from basal and alar plates, respectively) which innervate those structures derived from splanchnopleure. In addition, they supply the smooth muscle and glands of the somatopleure. These fibers are designated as follows:

a. *general visceral efferent*-These fibers will be considered under the *autonomic nervous system* later in this chapter.

b. *general visceral afferent*-Although the receptor endings of these fibers are located in the viscera, their fibers pass through the dorsal root of the spinal nerve as do the general somatic afferent fibers. Similarly, their cell bodies are located within the spinal ganglia and their central processes terminate in the intermediate portion of the alar plate.

B. Cranial nerves (Figs. 90,91,93)-The various segments of the brain and the nerves which arise therefrom are listed below. It should be noted that the distribution of fibers is described in general terms only. All craniospinal nerves are represented bilaterally.

1. Telencephalon-The *olfactory nerve* arises from this segment of the brain.

2. Diencephalon-The *optic nerve* arises from this segment and is actually a fiber tract of the brain.

3. Mesencephalon

a. *oculomotor nerve*-This nerve supplies muscles which are derived from the preotic somites, i.e. the extrinsic ocular muscles (superior, inferior, and medial recti and the inferior oblique eye muscles).

b. *trochlear nerve*-This nerve supplies the superior oblique muscle of the eye which is derived from a pre-otic somite.

158

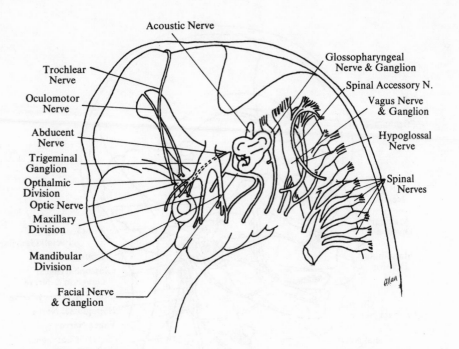

Acoustic Nerve

Trochlear Nerve

Oculomotor Nerve

Abducent Nerve

Trigeminal Ganglion

Opthalmic Division

Optic Nerve

Maxillary Division

Mandibular Division

Facial Nerve & Ganglion

Glossopharyngeal Nerve & Ganglion

Spinal Accessory N.

Vagus Nerve & Ganglion

Hypoglossal Nerve

Spinal Nerves

Allan

FIGURE **90.** Cranial and upper spinal nerves in a 15 mm. embryo (42 days). (after Hamilton, Boyd, and Mossman)

4. Metencephalon

　a. *trigeminal nerve*–This nerve consists of three large branches:

　　(1) *ophthalmic nerve*–This nerve has sensory endings in structures derived from the frontal process.

　　(2) *maxillary nerve*–The sensory innervation of those structures derived from the maxillary process is accomplished by this nerve.

　　(3) *mandibular nerve*–This nerve supplies both motor and sensory innervation to those structures which are derived from the mandibular or first branchial arch.

　b. *abducent nerve*–This nerve innervates the *lateral rectus* muscle of the eye which is derived from one of the pre-otic somites.

　c. *facial nerve*–This nerve innervates those structures derived from the hyoid or second branchial arch.

　d. *stato-acoustic* (*auditory*) *nerve*–Innervation of those structures derived from the otocyst is accomplished by this nerve via its subdivisions, the:

　　(1) *cochlear nerve*–This nerve supplies receptors for the organ of hearing (*spiral organ* or *organ of Corti*).

159

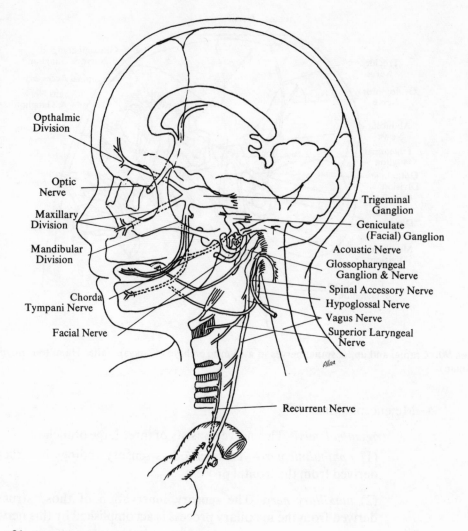

Opthalmic
Division

Optic
Nerve

Maxillary
Division

Mandibular
Division

Chorda
Tympani Nerve

Facial Nerve

Trigeminal
Ganglion

Geniculate
(Facial) Ganglion

Acoustic Nerve

Glossopharyngeal
Ganglion & Nerve

Spinal Accessory Nerve

Hypoglossal Nerve

Vagus Nerve

Superior Laryngeal
Nerve

Recurrent Nerve

FIGURE **91.** Cranial nerves in a full term fetus.

(2) *vestibular nerve*–This nerve supplies receptors for the organ of equilibration or balance (*semicircular ducts* or *canals*).

5. Myelencephalon

a. *glossopharyngeal nerve*–The structures derived from the third branchial arch are innervated by this nerve.

b. *vagus nerve*–This nerve sends fibers to those structures derived from the fourth, fifth, and sixth branchial arches. In addition it supplies fibers to the heart and derivatives of the foregut and midgut.

c. *accessory nerve*–The fibers constituting this nerve have two separate origins from the central nervous system.

160

(1) *cranial* portion of the nerve–This division innervates the muscles of the larynx, which are derived from the fourth, fifth. and sixth branchial arches. After its origin, it is intimately associated with the vagus nerve.

(2) *spinal* portion of the nerve–This division of the nerve actually arises from the upper three or four cervical segments of the spinal cord. It supplies the *sternocleidomastoideus* and *trapezius muscles*, which are apparently derived from the fifth through tenth somites.

d. *hypoglossal nerve*–Fibers of this nerve innervate the intrinsic muscles of the tongue which are derived from the first three or four (occipital) somites. These muscles migrate into the tongue after receiving their innervation and, therefore, carry the nerves with them during their migration.

C. Spinal nerves (Figs. 88,93)–The spinal cord gives rise to the segmental nerves which pass into the somite and supply the muscles, skin, etc., derived therefrom.

1. *Dorsal primary ramus*–Fibers from this ramus supply the muscles derived from the epimeres and the skin on the dorsal aspect of the body derived from the dermatome of the same segment.

2. *Ventral primary ramus*–These fibers supply the muscles derived from the hypomeres and the skin on the ventral aspect of the body located in the corresponding segment.

It should be noted that each spinal nerve is also associated with the *sympathetic trunk* (general visceral efferent system) via the *rami communicantes*. Thus fibers of the latter system are distributed to structures of segmental derivation by the spinal nerve where they supply the smooth muscle of vessels, the *erector pilae* muscles of hair follicles, and the sweat glands. On the other hand, the rami communicantes also serve as the route by which general visceral afferent fibers from the thoracic and abdominal viscera pass to the dorsal root of the spinal nerve.

III. Sympatho-Chromaffiin System

A. Autonomic nervous system (general visceral efferent system) (Figs. 92,93)

1. Definition–This system consists of a two-neuron chain which innervates all the viscera, smooth and cardiac muscle, and glands of the body. This essentially comprises those structures derived from the splanchnopleure, although it also includes the blood vessels and glands of the somatopleure.

2. Origin of components

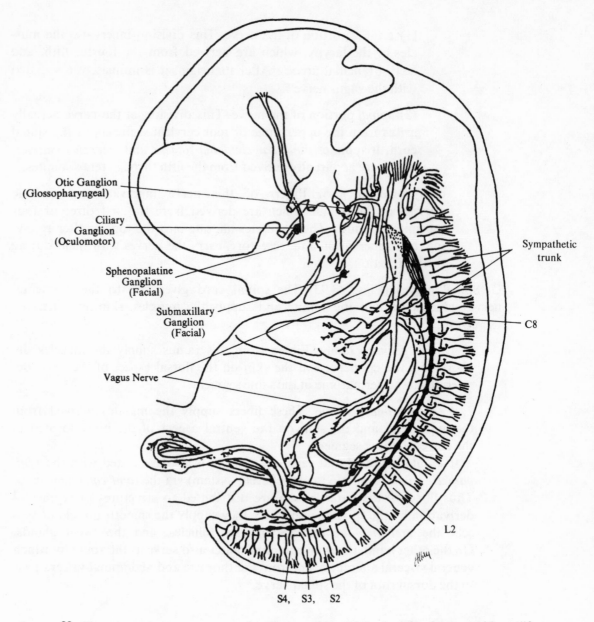

Otic Ganglion
(Glossopharyngeal)

Ciliary
Ganglion
(Oculomotor)

Sphenopalatine
Ganglion
(Facial)

Submaxillary
Ganglion
(Facial)

Vagus Nerve

Sympathetic
trunk

C8

L2

S4, S3, S2

FIGURE **92.** The autonomic nervous system of a 16 mm. embryo (43 days). (after Streeter, with modifications)

a. *preganglionic neuron*–This cell type arises in the central nervous system from cells in the intermediate zone of the gray matter (general visceral afferent column).

b. *postganglionic neuron*–Several theories have been advanced for the source of these cells and each has some supportive evidence. The possible sources are indicated below:

162

(1) neural crest–Cells from this source are thought to migrate from the crest into a position lateral to the aorta. There they form a chain of cells which later forms the ganglionated sympathetic chain.

(2) intermediate gray or the mantle layer of the basal plate–This has been described as a source of cells which migrate out the ventral root of the spinal nerve and then ventro-medially to form the sympathetic chain ganglia.

(3) ectodermal placodes–Cells from this source, in the cranial region, have been implicated in the formation of some of the cephalic autonomic ganglia.

2. Extension of components into the peripheral tissues–Regardless of their source, potential postganglionic cells migrate to a position essentially ventro-lateral to the vertebral column. There they form the paired sympathetic trunks or continue their migration to a position anterior to the aorta where they form pre-aortic ganglionic masses. Other cells of this origin migrate even farther along the visceral branches of the aorta and into the walls of the viscera, forming intramural ganglia. In order to establish connections with the ganglia thus formed, the preganglionic fibers extend from the central nervous system via the ventral root of the spinal nerve (or comparable root of a cranial nerve) and pass to the peripheral ganglion where they terminate or synapse with the postganglionic cell. The preganglionic fibers pass from the nervous system via two main routes.

a. *craniosacral outflow*–These fibers exit via cranial nerves three, seven, nine, and ten and sacral nerves two, *three,* and four. This is also called the *parasympathetic outflow.* Characteristically, the synapse with the postganglionic cell occurs within or very near the viscus innervated.

b. *thoracolumbar outflow*–This is also called the *sympathetic outflow* and its fibers exit the central nervous system via the spinal nerves in the thoracic and upper lumbar segments of the cord. Its synapses with postganglionic neurons occurs in the ganglia of the sympathetic trunk or in the pre-aortic ganglia.

B. Chromaffin system (Fig. 93)

1. Definition and description–This system is comprised of those cells with preganglionic innervation (thoracolumbar) which stain with chromate fixatives and are specialized for the elaboration of epinephrine and/or nor-epinephrine. It is embryologically, anatomically, and functionally related to the sympathetic division of the autonomic nervous system and, in many respects, its cells are comparable to a modified postganglionic sympathetic cell.

163

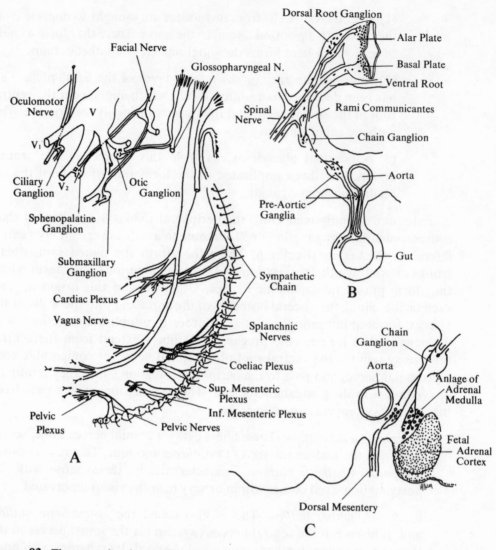

FIGURE 93. The sympatho-chromaffin system.
A. The autonomic nervous system as in Figure 92 in greater detail.
B. Cross section showing distribution of components of the sympathetic nervous system.
C. Formation of the adrenal medulla by migration of sympathetic elements.

2. Origin and migration of components–The cells which comprise this tissue have the same possible origins as the postganglionic elements of the thoracolumbar system. They migrate to a position closely associated with the aorta. The tissue is divisible into two types according to its ultimate location.

　　a. *suprarenal* (*adrenal*) *medulla*–A portion of the potential chromaffin tissue which is found in a para-aortic position migrates into the center of the *suprarenal* (*adrenal*) *cortical primordium* which is located

164

near the cranial end of the metanephros. The cells of the cortical primordium are derived from the coelomic mesothelium.

b. *extramedullary chromaffin bodies* (*paraganglia, chromaffin bodies, organs of Zuckerkandl*)–Tissues comprising these scattered bodies can be identified along the sympathetic chains and their branches. They are also associated with the abdominal aorta or its major branches. Apparently most of this tissue degenerates during postnatal life.

IV. Function of the Nervous System in Prenatal Life

This is an area in which relatively little is known, especially in the human fetus. However, certain generalizations regarding activity of the fetus in this period can be established.

A. *General activities*–Activity of the nervous system in an embryo is first indicated as reflex activity mediated by the spinal cord. The appearance of these reflexes are as follows:

1. Response to tactile (touch) stimuli–This is seen in the human fetus at about eight weeks (25mm. crown-rump length).

2. Spontaneous fetal activity–Spontaneous movements are observed at nine or ten weeks (25–40 mm. crown-rump length).

3. Movements detectable by mother–This observation can usually be made at 16 weeks.

B. Specific activities

1. *Palmar* (*grasp*) and *plantar* (*Babinski*) reflexes–These are present at the end of the third intra-uterine month of life.

2. *Respiratory, sucking,* and *swallowing* reflexes–These reflexes are well established at birth.

3. *Reflex eye movements* and the *pupillary reflex* to light–These reflexes are both operative at birth.

18

Organs of the Special Senses

I. Olfactory Organs (Fig. 94)

A. *Olfactory placodes*–These are plates of thickened ectoderm on the ventral aspect of the frontal process. They appear late in the fourth week.

B. *Olfactory pits*–The placodes become depressed and located within the olfactory pits. The pits are separated in the midline by the medial nasal process and are bounded laterally by the lateral nasal processes. A description of the fate of these processes and the separation of the nasal cavity from the stomodeum is presented in earlier chapters, especially Chapter 10.

C. *Olfactory epithelium*–This tissue is formed from the placode within the pit and is established as the *olfactory nerve cells* differentiate and send processes centrally into the olfactory bulb of the telencephalon.

II. Gustatory Organs

These organs are first noted as localized thickenings of the lingual epithelium and epithelium of the palate and pharynx. The thickened epithelium in these areas gives rise to the *taste buds* and develops in areas associated with nerve terminations of the seventh, ninth, and tenth cranial nerves. The nerves supply sensory terminations (taste buds) in those portions of the tongue, palate, and pharynx which are derived from the branchial arch with which the nerve is associated (see Chapter 17).

III. Development of the Eye

A. Development of the retinal primordia (Figs. 94,95,96)

1. *Optic sulci*–These grooves are first noted in the cephalic portion of the neural plate of early somite embryos. The grooves mark the site at which an evagination occurs which gives rise to the:

166

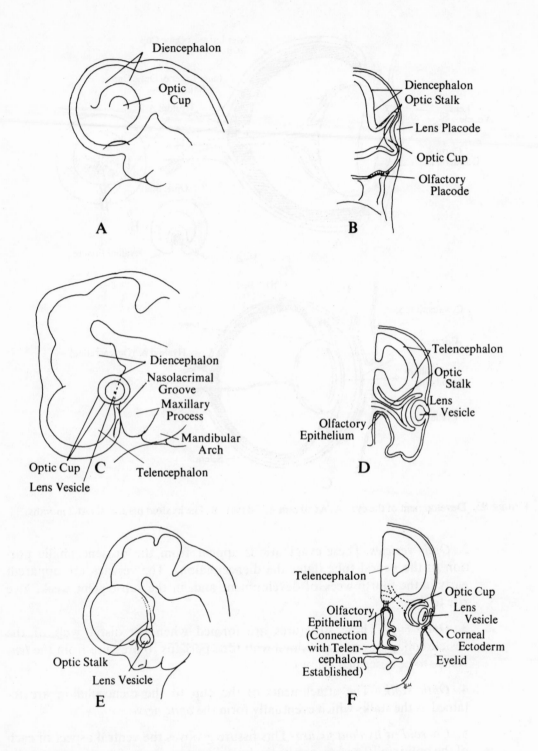

FIGURE **94.** Development of the eye. (Note also the olfactory primordia).
A and B. Lateral and frontal views respectively at 4 mm. (30 days). C and D. Lateral and frontal views respectively at 7 mm. (34 days). E and F. Corresponding views at 2 months.

167

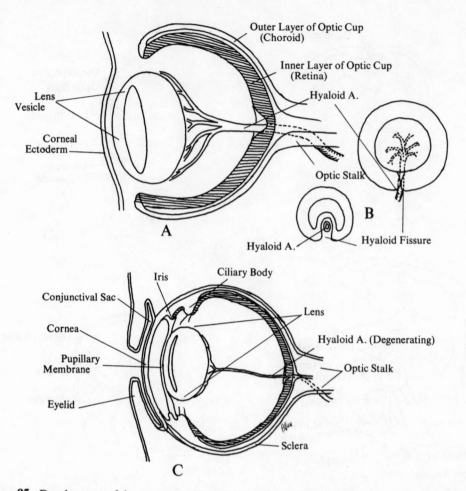

FIGURE 95. Development of the eye. A. At 10 mm. (37 days). B. The hyaloid fissure. C. At 2 months.

2. *Optic vesicles*–These evaginations appear from the prosencephalic portion of the neural tube (later the diencephalon). The vesicles are apparent early in the fourth week of development and, in the subsequent week, give rise to the:

3. *Optic cups*–These structures are formed when the distal wall of the vesicle collapses on its proximal wall (due perhaps to pressure from the *lens vesicle* to be described below).

4. *Optic stalks*–The attachments of the cup to the diencephalon are retained as the stalks which eventually form the *optic nerve.*

5. *Choroid* or *hyaloid fissure*–This fissure grooves the ventral aspect of each of the optic stalks and transmits the hyaloid artery. Each fissure is eventually closed by fusion of its edges below the artery, thus enclosing the latter within the stalk and cup.

168

B. Differentiation of the optic nerve and retina (Figs. 94,95,96)

  1. Optic cup

    a. outer (proximal) layer–This portion of the cup gives rise to the *pigmented layer* of the *retina*. The lumen of the vesicle is obliterated by the fusion of the outer and inner layers of the cup.

    b. inner (distal) layer–This layer of the cup becomes the *visual* or *optic* portion of the retina and near its union with the outer layer forms the *ciliary* and *iridial* portions of the retina. Neither the ciliary portion nor the iridial portion has photoreceptive cells.

  2. Optic stalk–The stalk is converted into the optic nerve after cells from the inner layer of the optic cup (visual retina) grow through the stalk to the diencephalon. The so-called optic nerve is, therefore, actually a fiber tract of the brain.

C. Development of the lens (Figs. 94,95,96)

  1. *Lens placode*–In the middle of the fifth week of development a thickening in the ectoderm overlying the optic vesicle gives rise to this plate. Shortly after its formation it becomes depressed and forms the:

  2. *Lens vesicle*–This ectodermal sphere sinks beneath, and separates from, the overlying ectoderm. It is intimately associated with the distal layer of the optic vesicle at this point and is carried into the mouth of the optic cup as that structure is formed. Changes in the cells which constitute this vesicle result in the formation of the:

  3. *Definitive lens*–This structure is constructed of the elongated *lens fibers*, derived from the deep or internal layer of the lens vesicle, and the *lens capsule* which is derived from the superficial layer of the vesicle.

D. *Choroid, sclera,* and *cornea* (Figs. 95,96)–These layers of the eye may be compared to the meninges of the brain. They serve as coverings for the light-sensitive elements of the eye and are derived from the mesenchyme which surrounds it. The innermost, vascular layer is the:

  1. Choroid–This layer is intimately associated with the pigment (outermost) layer of the retina. It appears at the end of the second month and, in the subsequent two weeks, forms both of the following:

    a. *ciliary body*–This structure consists essentially of the thickened choroid at the margin of the optic cup. It becomes attached to and controls the shape of the lens. This is possible by muscles which develop within the body. Its internal surface is covered by the ciliary portion of the retina.

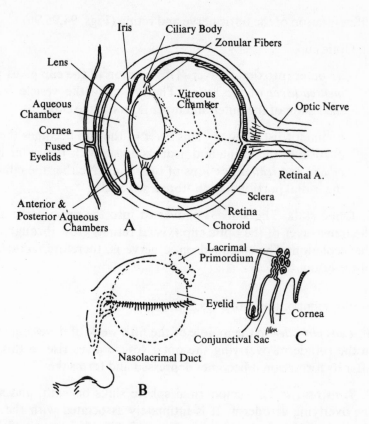

FIGURE **96.** Development of the eye completed. A. At 9 weeks. B. Frontal view showing lacrimal apparatus. C. Cross section of eyelid and conjunctival sac at birth.

       b. *iris*–This is a compound structure derived primarily from the choroid but also containing ectodermal elements which give rise to its muscles. It is covered on its internal surface by the iridial portion of the retina.

    2. Sclera–This covering of the eye is external to the choroid and is formed by a tougher, denser layer of mesenchyme which eventually becomes fibrous in nature. It is the outermost layer of the eyeball and serves as the layer to which the extrinsic muscles of the eye attach.

    3. Cornea–Within the edges of the optic cup and between the lens and the overlying ectoderm a tough transparent membrane, the cornea, is found. It is continuous with the sclera and gains an ectodermal layer which is continuous with that lining the eyelids (*conjunctiva*) which will be described below.

  E. Chambers of the eye (Figs. 95,96)

    1. *Vitreous chamber*–This chamber is derived from the space between the lens vesicle and the optic cup. It is filled with a jelly-like substance which

170

is associated with the hyaloid vessels. The substance is apparently derived, at least in part, from mesenchyme trapped in the optic cup. It becomes the *vitreous humor* of the adult eye. The hyaloid artery, which passes through the vitreous humor, degenerates by birth, leaving the *hyaloid canal* to indicate its former position.

2. *Aqueous chamber*–The interval between the lens and the cornea contains mesenchyme which breaks down to form the cavity of the aqueous chamber. The chamber is divided peripherally into the *anterior* and *posterior chambers* by the iris. The anterior and posterior chambers communicate via the pupil which is formed by the free central edge of the iris.

F. Accessory structures of the eye (Figs. 95,96)

1. *Eyelids*–These structures appear at seven weeks as ectodermal folds superior and inferior to the cornea and later extend anterior to that structure. The lids are separated from the cornea by the ectoderm-lined *conjunctival sac*. The free margins of the lids fuse during the early part of the third month. The fusion breaks down by the fifth month, permitting the lid to be opened.

2. *Lacrimal glands*–From the conjunctival sac, epithelial outgrowths form the primordium of this gland. These outgrowths appear especially from the dorso-lateral extensions of the sac.

3. Extrinsic muscles of the eye–The origin of these muscles was considered in Chapter 15.

IV. Development of the Auditory and Vestibular Apparatus

A. *Internal ear* (Figs. 97,98,99)–This structure contains the neural receptors for hearing and equilibrium or balance which are ultimately derived from the:

1. *Otic placode*–This structure appears as a thickening of head ectoderm opposite the rhombencephalon (metencephalon) of early (seven) somite embryos. It sinks beneath the surface becoming, in succession, the *otic pit,* and at thirty somites, the:

2. *Otic vesicle* or *otocyst*–This vesicle is intimately related to the neural crest in this region. In this position portions of the facial and stato-acoustic nerves arise from cells of the crest. Bipolar nerve cells of the stato-acoustic nerves connect neuro-epithelial receptor cells derived from certain cells of the otocyst with the rhombencephalon. The otocyst becomes divided into the following:

a. *cochlear portion*–This portion gives rise to the epithelium (*membranous labyrinth*) of the *cochlear canal* or *duct* and the *saccule*.

171

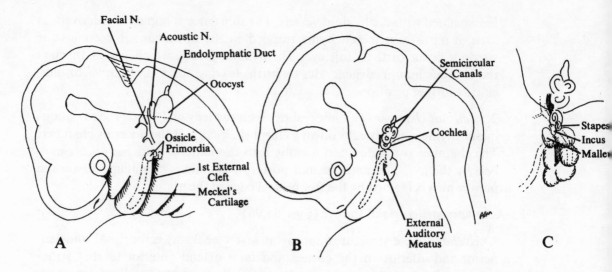

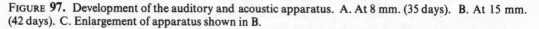

FIGURE **97.** Development of the auditory and acoustic apparatus. A. At 8 mm. (35 days). B. At 15 mm. (42 days). C. Enlargement of apparatus shown in B.

  b. *vestibular portion*–This portion becomes the epithelium (membranous labyrinth) of the *semicircular ducts (canals)* and of the *utricle*.

  It should be observed that only certain portions of the membranous labyrinth derived from the otocyst differentiate the specialized neuro-epithelial receptor cell.

  c. *endolymphatic duct*–This is a diverticulum of the otocyst that appears early in development and is retained as the *endolymphatic sac*.

  The membranous labyrinth and endolymphatic duct are filled with the *endolymph*.

3. *Otic capsule*–This structure is actually part of the petrous portion of the temporal bone. It arises as a condensation of mesenchyme which surrounds the otic vesicle or otocyst. It becomes chondrified and ultimately ossified. Prior to ossification, however, the cartilage immediately adjacent to the otocyst (membranous labyrinth) becomes eroded and forms thereby the:

4. *Peri-otic space (perilymphatic space)*–This space between the bony and membranous labyrinth becomes modified differently in the cochlear and vestibular regions and, as a consequence, can be further described in relation to each. It is filled with a fluid, the *perilymph*.

  a. cochlear portion–The peri-otic space related to the cochlear duct is divided into an upper canal (*scala vestibuli*) and a lower canal (*scala tympani*). The wall of the cochlear duct adjacent to the scala tympani becomes the specialized *spiral organ (organ of Corti)* which contains the receptor cells noted above.

172

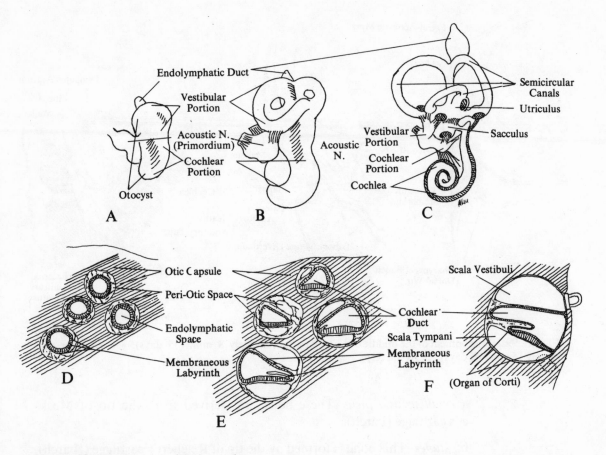

FIGURE **98.** Development of the internal ear.

A, B, and C are from embryos of 9 mm. (36 days), 13 mm. (40 days), and 30 mm. (2 months) respectively. Neuro-epithelial elements are indicated in C as cross hatch areas.

D, E, and F represents stages in development of the cochlear apparatus (cross sections) at 30 mm. (2 months), 50 mm. (10 weeks), and approximately 5 months.

b. vestibular portion–The peri-otic space retains a more primitive relationship to the membranous labyrinth of this derivative of the otocyst and is called simply the perilymphatic space.

B. *Middle ear* or *tympanum* (Fig. 99)

1. *Tubotympanic diverticulum*–This diverticulum consists of a dorsal prolongation of the first pharyngeal pouch. It is lined by endoderm and gives rise to a dilated *tympanic cavity* (tympanum) at its distal end. The portion of the diverticulum between the tympanum and the pharynx becomes the *auditory* (*pharyngotympanic* or *eustachian*) *tube*.

2. Ossicles of the middle ear–These small bones are derived from the primitive cartilaginous skeletons of the first and second branchial arches. The ossicles and their derivations are as follows:

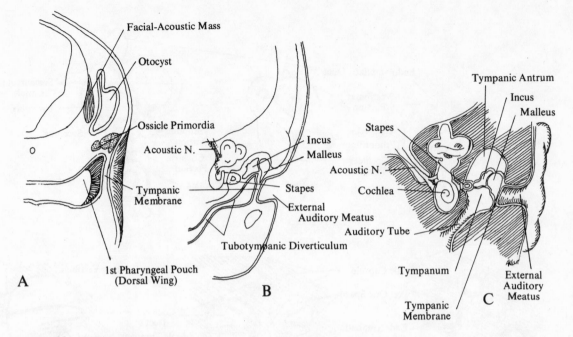

FIGURE **99.** Development of the middle ear. A. At approximately 8 mm. (35 days). B. At approximately 15 mm. (42 days). C. At full term.

a. *malleus* and *incus*–These bones are derived from the tip of Meckel's cartilage (I arch).

b. *stapes*–This bone is formed by the tip of Reichert's cartilage (II arch).

3. Muscles of the middle ear–These muscles are also derived from the mesoderm of adjacent branchial arches.

a. *tensor tympani*–This muscle is derived from the first branchial arch and is innervated therefore by a branch of the trigeminal nerve.

b. *stapedius*–This muscle is derived from the second branchial arch and is innervated by a branch of the facial nerve.

Both ossicles and muscles are located at first in the wall of the tympanum but, as the latter expands, they come to lie within the cavity. In a more exact sense, however, they are still excluded from it by their covering of endoderm which lines that cavity. The expansion of the tympanum into the mastoid portion of the temporal bone gives origin to the *mastoid air cells.*

C. *External ear* (Figs. 97,100)

1. *Tympanic membrane*–This structure consists of the apposed layers of ectoderm and endoderm of the first pharyngeal groove (cleft) and pouch, respectively, with a small amount of intervening mesenchyme.

174

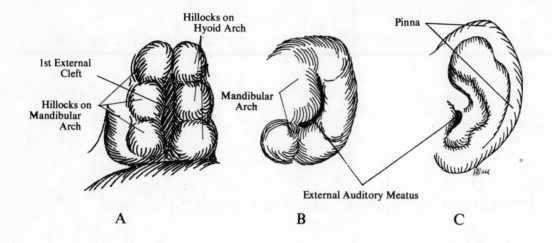

Hillocks on
Hyoid Arch

1st External
Cleft

Hillocks on
Mandibular
Arch

Mandibular
Arch

Pinna

External Auditory Meatus

A   B   C

FIGURE **100.** Development of the external ear. A. At 10 mm. (37 days). B. At 20 mm. (47 days). C. At full term.

2. *External auditory meatus*–This canal is derived from the first external pharyngeal groove.

3. *Auricle* (*Pinna*)–This structure is developed from hillocks or swellings adjacent to the first pharyngeal groove that are derived from the first and second branchial arches.

175

19

Integumentary System and Associated Structures

I. Introduction

The structures to be considered in this chapter are, in major part, derived from the ectoderm. However, the underlying mesoderm contributes to the formation of each structure under consideration.

II. *Skin (cutis) (Fig. 101)*

A. *Epidermis*–This is the outer layer of the skin and is of ectodermal origin. At first a single layer of cells, at the beginning of the second month it becomes bilaminar, then multilaminar by the multiplicative efforts of the ectodermal cells. In the last half of fetal life, definitive stratification occurs with the formation of the characteristic layers (*stratum basale* or *germinativum, granulosum, lucidum,* and *corneum,* from internal to external).

At birth the skin is covered by a cheesy material called the *vernix caseosa.* This material is formed by desquamated superficial layers of the epidermis, fetal hair, and the products of the glands of the skin.

An additional cellular element of the epidermis is the *melanoblast* which migrates into this position from the neural crest from which it takes origin. These cells produce *melanin* which is responsible, in part, for the color of the skin.

176

B. *Dermis* (*corium*)–This is the deep layer of the skin which is derived from mesoderm and serves as the means by which the epidermis is nourished, innervated, and attached to the muscular and skeletal elements of the body. As has been noted in earlier chapters, the dermis is derived, at least in part, from the dermatome which is, in turn, a derivative of the somite. The skin receives innervation from the segmental nerves, each of the latter supplying that segment of the dermis (and the overlying epidermis) derived from a particular dermatome. At the end of the second month the simple mesenchyme just under the epidermis becomes fibrillar and projects into the epidermis. These projections form the:

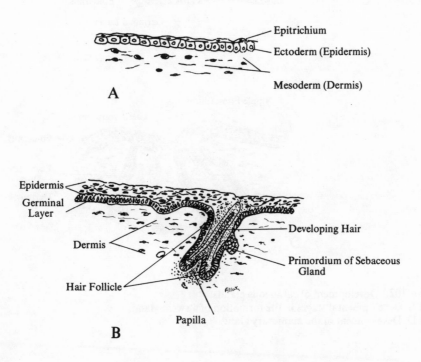

FIGURE **101.** Development of the skin and hair. A. The skin in third month. B. Skin at term showing developing hair follicle.

177

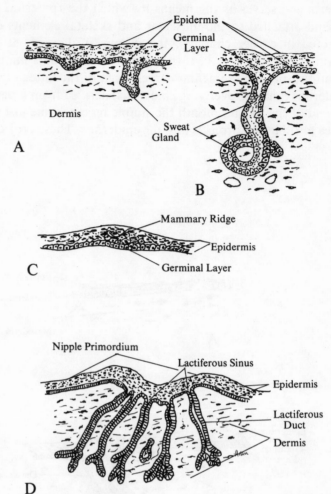

FIGURE **102.** Development of cutaneous glands.
A and B. Developmental stages in the formation of a sweat gland.
C and D. Development of the mammary gland.

1. *Dermal papillae*–These structures contain blood vessels and/or end organs or receptors of sensory nerves.

2. *Papillary ridges*–These are more regular, linear elevations of the dermis into the epidermis which are well established by birth. Although present in a definable pattern over the entire body, they are especially prominent on the palmar surface of fingers and hand, where they are called *fingerprints*. Similar patterns are found on the plantar surface of the toes and feet.

III. Associated Structures

In a sense, the structures considered below are derived from or are an integral part of the skin. Nevertheless, certain characteristics qualify them for separate consideration.

A. *Glands of the skin* (Fig. 102)–These small organs appear as invaginations of the ectoderm (stratum germinativum) which burrow into the dermis. There are several types which are listed below:

1. *Sebaceous glands*–These glands often arise as a bud or outgrowth of the epidermis liining the hair follicle. They appear during the latter part of the fourth month and produce an oily secretion during the last trimester of pre-natal life.

2. *Sweat (sudoriporous) glands*–These glands appear at the fourth month as epithelial cords which later canalize. They become enlarged and specialized in certain areas, i.e. axilla, external auditory meatus, and eyelids.

3. *Mammary glands*–These glands are said to be specialized sweat glands, although their primordia appear early in the sixth week of development. This precedes the appearance of typical sweat glands by several weeks. Nevertheless, characteristics of the mammary gland mark it as related to the sweat glands. The primordia of the glands form thickened strips of ectoderm located bilaterally from axilla to groin which are called the *milk ridges* or *lines*. The cranial portion of each ridge forms a localized thickening of the epidermal cells which send fifteen to twenty cords of cells (*Primary milk ducts)* into the underlying dermis. The cords become canalized and continue to invade the fatty, superficial fascia which attaches the skin to the deeper structures. A hollowing of the epidermis at the site of the original ingrowth produces a common sinus (*lactiferous sinus*) into which open the ducts formed from the canalized cords. Later, an area immediately surrounding the sinus becomes somewhat pigmented to form the *areola* and the central portion somewhat elevated to form the *nipple*.

At birth, the fetal breast is incompletely established although it often shows pseudo-secretory activity. This is due, perhaps, to the stimulus of maternal hormones reaching the infant via the placenta. Completion of its differentiation, however, awaits the changes coincident with puberty and pregnancy.

B. Nails (Fig. 103)–These structures are first indicated by the *nail fields* or *beds* which appear on the dorsum of each digit bounded by the *nail folds* proximally and laterally. In the hand, these structures are well defined at ten weeks. They appear slightly later on the toes. Cornification of the epidermis of the nail bed gives rise to a *false nail* in the fourth month. The false nail is replaced by the definitive *nail plate* which arises within the *matrix* of the proximal nail

179

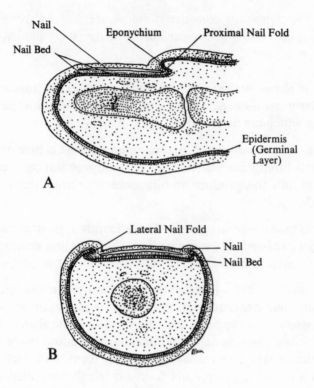

Nail

Eponychium

Proximal Nail Fold

Nail Bed

Epidermis
(Germinal
Layer)

A

Lateral Nail Fold

Nail

Nail Bed

B

FIGURE **103.** Development of the nail (at midfetal life). A. Midsagittal section. B. Cross section.

fold during the following month. The differentiation or formation of the nail extends from the base of the fold to a point in the nail bed called the *lunula* and is marked by the whitish "moons" at the base of the nails. Growth of the nail plate continues during fetal life and reaches the tip of the digit in the month prior to birth.

The extension of the epidermis of the nail fold upon the nail constitutes the *eponychium*, whereas similar tissue under the tip of the nail is called the *hyponychium*.

C. Hair (Fig. 101)–The primordium of the *hair follicle,* which gives rise to the hair, appears as an invagination of the germinal layer of the epidermis. This invagination occurs during the third month of development and, at this time, follicles are apparent in the eyebrows, lips, and chin. As each follicle extends into the dermis, it gains a connective tissue sheath and its base becomes enlarged to form the *hair bulb,* which is invaginated by the mesenchymal *papilla* of the hair. The epidermal cells of the bulb associated with the papilla form the core of the hair. Additional layers are added to the core and consist of cornified cells from the *sheath cells* of the follicle, i.e. those cells above the bulb. Pigment of the hair is derived from melanoblasts and is carried into the hair by cells of the bulb.

180

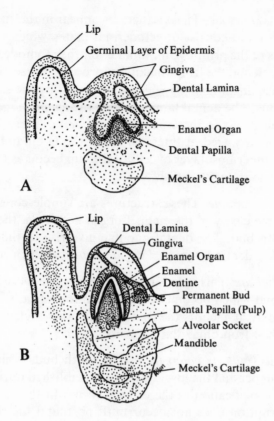

FIGURE **104.** Development of the teeth. A. Early stage of tooth bud development. B. Later stage of tooth bud development.

The follicles make their appearance over the surface of the body during the fourth month and produce the fetal hair (*lanugo*) during the following month. The lanugo is shed and has virtually disappeared at birth. The hair of postnatal life develops gradually from new or reorganized follicles. The changes in the pubic, axillary, and general body hair which occur during puberty are due to the influence of sex hormones.

III.   Teeth (Fig. 104)

Although intimately associated with the digestive tract, and, indeed, sometimes considered to be accessory organs of the digestive system, the teeth are derived from stomodeal ectoderm and its supporting mesoderm. For this reason, teeth are considered with the integument. In the human, two sets of teeth make their appearance. Each has a similar origin from primordia which are established during embryonic and fetal life.

181

A. Dental primordia

1. *Dental laminae*–These structures appear in the sixth week of development (11 mm.) and consist of ectodermal plates which rim the upper and lower margins of the primitive mouth, i.e. on the stomodeal surfaces of the mandibular arch and the frontomaxillary process. These laminae appear just internal to the *labial laminae* which are formed by the same arches and give rise to the lips. The dental laminae form the *enamel organs* each of which is one component of the *tooth bud* or *tooth germ.* The enamel organs appear as swellings arranged at intervals along the lamina. They form inverted cups and the innermost layer of cells of the cup becomes the columnar *ameloblasts* which elaborate the *enamel.*

2. *Dental papillae*–These structures are simple cones of mesenchyme which invade the cavity of the enamel organ and form, thereby, the second part of the tooth bud. The dental papillae give rise to the *dentine* and *pulp* of the teeth. The dentine is formed by *odontoblasts* which cover the papillary cone.

3. *Dental sac*–This structure is formed by the loose mesenchyme around the tooth bud which becomes organized into a sheath for the developing tooth. Ultimately, it anchors the tooth to the bony socket formed by the mandibular arch or frontomaxillary process.

B. *Deciduous* (*milk or baby*) *teeth*–The tooth buds which form these teeth (ten in both the upper and the lower jaws) are established during the tenth week of development. Calcification of these buds occurs in the fourth intra-uterine month and their eruption does not occur until postnatal life (beginning at six months and continuing to the third year). These teeth are shed between six and eleven years and are replaced by the:

C. *Permanent teeth*–The tooth buds giving rise to these teeth appear on the internal aspect of the buds for the deciduous teeth. They are derived from the dental lamina and associated mesoderm in the manner noted above. There are thirty-two buds for permanent teeth and the appearance of these primordia does not occur until the fifth intra-uterine month and calcification does not begin until postnatal life. Eruption of the permanent teeth awaits the shedding of the deciduous teeth (actually, they are probably responsible for shedding of the latter) and occurs from the sixth postnatal year into the third decade of life. Growth of each tooth is essentially completed when eruption takes place.

20

Teratology—Abnormal Development

I. Introduction

Variation in biological structure is very common, indeed, one might say, the rule. In greater part these variations are slight and fall within the arbitrary limits of that which is called normal. *Teratology* is the study of defective development— a study of conditions where variations in an individual's development are beyond the range of normalcy. An anomaly or anomalies can be found in about 8 per cent of all bodies which come to autopsy, although only 2 per cent of live infants show obvious external malformations. However, abnormalities of stillborn infants are more frequently noted.

II. Etiology

The cause of abnormal development is incompletely understood, but it is known to be influenced by hereditary or genetic factors, environmental influences, and the interaction of the two preceding factors.

A. *Genetic factors*-The belief that many congenital anomalies have a genic basis has long been held, although the mechanism thereof has not been understood— hence, references to tainted blood, etc. through medieval and even biblical writings. The genetic etiology has at least two primary possible answers:

1. Mutation-There are many possible explanations for this phenomenon including the effect of radiation. The result is a change in the gene structure and, consequently, in the structure(s) which may be influenced by that gene.

2. Interaction of recessive genes-Recessive genes were probably mutants at one time which are dominated by the corresponding "normal" gene of a pair. However, when such a gene appears in both parents, the effect may be apparent in the offspring.

B. Environmental factors–Although a fetus is relatively well protected from extrinsic noxious influences by the placental barrier, nevertheless, it is being found that a number of extrinsic factors can bypass the barrier and have a profound effect upon the development of the embryo.

1. *Congenital disease*

a. *maternal infection*–In certain conditions in which a maternal infection exists, toxins produced by the infection may pass to the fetus. It may also be that the condition so effects maternal physiology as to result in fetal maldevelopment.

b. *fetal infection*–This is a condition in which pathogenic organisms directly affect the embryo or fetus proper.

2. *Nutritional aspects* of abnormal development–The concept that the fetus is a true parasite and can exact all it needs from the mother is not entirely true. Good evidence that poor maternal nutrition is a cause of abnormal development exists. Recent experiments which selectively block certain vitamins have been found to produce quite specific abnormalities. Other substances have been shown to be teratogenic because, perhaps, of the disruption of basic metabolic activities. All these observations lend support to the importance of malnutrition on abnormal development.

C. *Immunological factors*–Incompatability of maternal and fetal blood types (Rh factor) may result in destruction of fetal blood cells with resultant anoxia, and so forth. It is possible that other responses to foreign protein in the fetus might occur and have a deleterious effect on development.

III. Types of Abnormal Development (Figs. 105,106,109,110,111,112)

A. Agenesis–This condition results from the failure of primordia to appear at the appropriate moment or phase of the developmental process. Examples of this may be seen in the skeleton (absence of limbs or digits) or may involve certain organs such as the kidney or the gonad.

B. *Developmental arrests*–In conditions of this nature the primordium appears but, for one reason or another, retains a primitive state to a greater or lesser degree. Subdivision of this category and examples are listed below:

1. *Hypoplasia*–This is a condition in which growth is inadequate.

a. localized–This condition effects a particular organ or structure (*penile hypoplasia*, hypoplasia of a limb, etc.).

b. generalized–This condition results in a proportional failure of growth and is typified by true *dwarfism*.

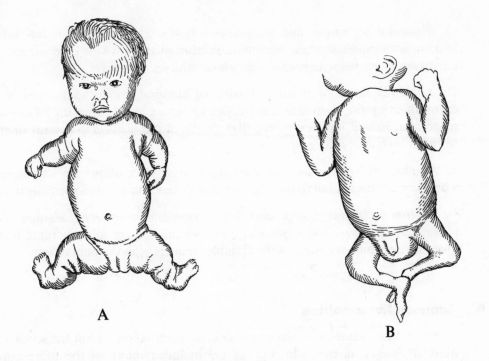

A   B

FIGURE **105.** (after Potter, *Pathology of the Fetus and the Newborn*, Yearbook Publishers, Inc.). A. Achondroplasia. B. Hypoplasia of the lower extremity.

2. *Retention of primitive conditions*–Maldevelopment of this sort can involve either visceral or somatic structures.

> a. viscera—*Duodenal atresia* (occlusion), *duplex uteri, rectovaginal fistula* are examples of this condition.

> b. soma–It should be noted here that many of the conditions falling in this category might be classified as *midline defects* or failure of structures of a bilateral nature to undergo normal fusion. Examples are *cleft palate, umbilical herniation, bifid sternum. Syndactyly* is a condition in which the digits are fused with one another as in the primitive condition.

3. *Failure to undergo normal atrophy*–In this condition, structures that normally obliterate or disappear are retained. For example, *persistent anal membrane, imperforate hymen,* persistence of the *vaginal process* of peritoneum, *double vena cava, persistent ductus arteriosus.*

4. *Failure to consolidate*–This situation results in *lobed* or *accessory* organs such as the *spleen, pancreas,* or *adrenal glands.*

5. *Incomplete migration*–In certain anomalies, organs that normally undergo a change of position fail to do so. Examples of this are *undescended testicles, unascended kidneys,* and *lingual thyroid glands.*

185

C. *Abnormal migration* and *misplacement–Migration* of the *ovary* into the labia majora (mimicking the normal migration of the testis) is an example of this condition as are *thoracic parathyroid glands* and *palatine teeth*.

D. *Abnormal fusion or splitting*–Fusion of bilateral organs sometimes occur as exemplified by the *horseshoe kidney*. On the other hand, splitting of organ primordia or, indeed, the embryonic disc results in duplication of organs or the entire embryo (*twinning*), respectively.

E. *Atypical differentiation–Achondroplasia* and *mongolism* are conditions in which certain tissues fail to undergo normal differentiation and specialization.

F. *Atavism* (ancestral recurrences)–The *azygos lobe of the lung, elevator muscles of the clavicle, vermiform appendix,* and *cervical ribs* are all structures found in lower forms which reappear, with variable frequency, in the human fetus.

IV. Common Abnormalities

To list all the examples of abnormal development is not within the scope of this book. However, in the following list are included many of the more common anomalies and conditions and the significant features of such anomalies.

A. Abnormalities affecting the organism as a whole (usually the result of the lack of hormones affecting all cells and tissues).

1. Dwarfism–This condition is usually not apparent until sometime after birth. It is considered here because it has been demonstrated that a major cause of this condition is developmental failure of the hormone-producing organs that effect growth (thyroid and hypophysis).

a. *Cretinism–*This type of dwarfism is due to deficient thyroid function.

b. *Peter Pan type–*This is due to pituitary insufficiency.

2. *Gigantism–*The formation of excessively large infants may be due to excess production of growth hormone from the pituitary.

B. Abnormalities of particular organ systems
It should be noted here that some anomalies involve several organ systems due to the interaction of developmental processes, i.e. one tissue awaits differentiation, migration, etc., until an adjacent tissue has accomplished its differentiation or migration. If the earlier differentiating tissue or structure fails to do so, it may prevent normal development of dependent tissues or structures. Insofar as is possible, such anomalies, e.g. *spina bifida*, will be described with the organ system in which the developmental failure is initiated.

1. Anomalies of the cardiovascular system–Abnormalities in this category constitute 10 per cent of all abnormalities (Fig. 106, 107, 108)

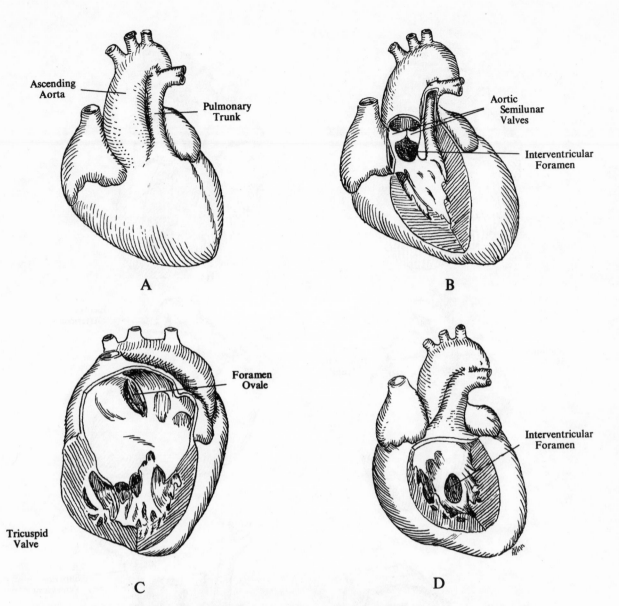

FIGURE **106.** Septal defects. A. and B. External and internal views of the heart demonstrating the tetralogy of Fallot. C. Patent foramen ovale. D. Interventricular septal defect.

a. cardiac anomalies–These are usually due to arrested development and vary from the extreme to very slight defects.

(1) incomplete septation of the heart
   (a) complete absence of the septa (*cor biloculare*)
   (b) absence or gross defect of the interventricular septum (*cor triloculare*)
   (c) partial interventricular septal defect (*patent interventricular foramen*)

187

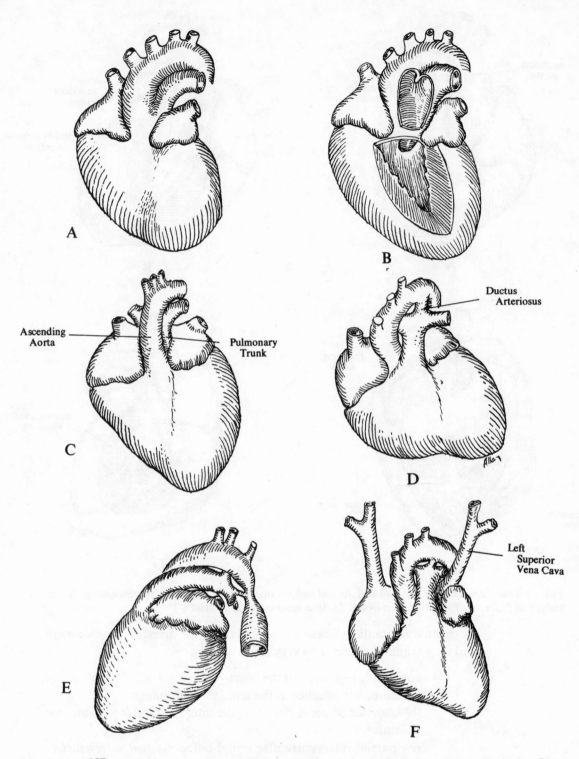

Ascending
Aorta

Pulmonary
Trunk

Ductus
Arteriosus

Left
Superior
Vena Cava

FIGURE 107. A. Persistent truncus arteriosus—Exterior view. B. Persistent truncus arteriosus—Interior view of truncal region (Note absence of bulbar ridges.) C. Dextroposition of the aorta. D. Patent ductus arteriosus. E. Coarctation of the aorta. F. Double superior vena cava.

188

(d) interatrial septal defect (*patent foramen ovale*)

(2) *heterotaxis* (abnormal position or development)
(a) this may be simple reversal of the heart or may include all the viscera (*dextrocardia* and *situs inversus*)
(b) incomplete descent from cervical region
(c) displacement of heart outside the thorax (*ectopic cordis*)

(3) valvular defects
(a) *atresia* or *stenosis*, i.e. narrowing of the interval between valves
(b) *supernumerary valves*

(4) congenital tumors of the heart

b. anomalies involving the great arteries

(1) persistence of fetal ducts (*patent ductus arteriosus*)

(2) aortico-bulbar septal defects
(a) absence of the septum with a *persistent truncus arteriosus*
(b) partial defects of the septum

(3) transposition
(a) associated with transposition of the heart (as in dextro-cardia or situs inversus)
(b) aorta and pulmonary trunks arising from right and left ventricles, respectively

(4) aortic arch variations
(a) doubled aorta–This is the result of the persistence of the right fourth aortic arch.
(b) right aortic arch–Right fourth aortic arch persists, whereas the left arch obliterates.
(c) variations in the origin and course of the subclavian and carotid arteries–A great number of variations are possible but can be explained on the basis of retention of portions of the primitive aortic arches which usually obliterate.
(d) *coarctation of aorta*–Stenosis or atresia of the descending aorta (usually at the site of its juncture with the ductus arteri-osus)
(e) abnormalities in origin of the coronary arteries from the aorta

c. anomalies involving the great veins

(1) persistent left superior vena cava–This anomaly appears, when the normal cross anastomosis with the right superior vena cava fails to occur.

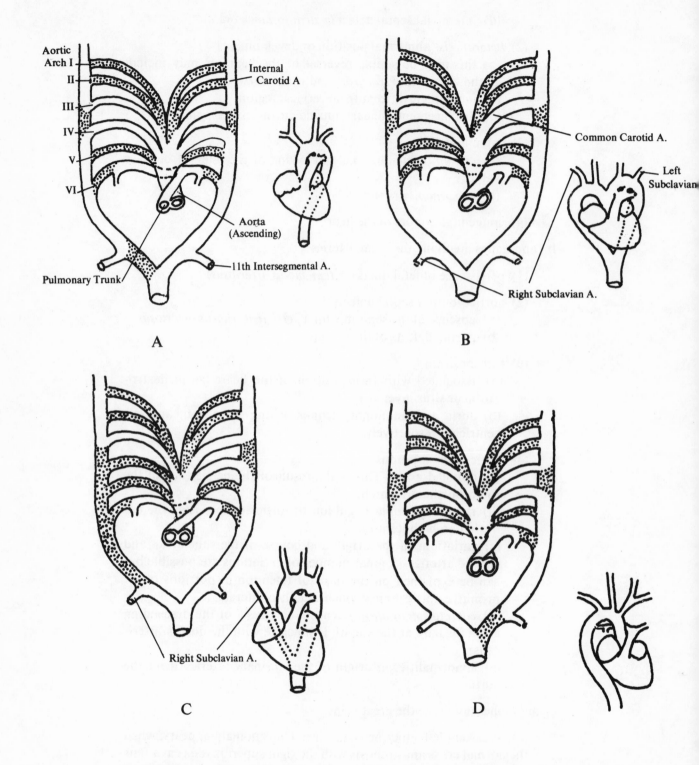

FIGURE 108. Anomalies of the aortic arches. A. Normal pattern of obliteration of the aortic arches. B. Doubled aortic arch. C. Anomalous right subclavian artery. D. Right aortic arch.

190

(2) incomplete absorption of the sinus venosus into the right atrium

(3) patency of the ductus venosus and/or the umbilical vein

d. several clinical entities exist which may include several of the abnormalities listed above. For example, the *tetralogy of Fallot* includes stenosis of the pulmonary artery, overriding of the interventricular septum by the aorta, patent interventricular foramen, and an enlarged right ventricle.

2. Anomalies of the digestive tract (Figs. 109,110,111)

a. abnormalities associated with stomodeal structures

(1) incomplete fusion of the maxillary process with adjacent processes results in:
(a) *harelip*–This is a failure of the maxillary process and nasal processes to fuse and can occur uni- or bilaterally.
(b) *cleft palate*–This is the result of the failure of the palatine processes of the maxillary arch to fuse in the midline.

(2) *Rathke's pouch persistence*–This forms the *craniopharyngeal canal* with occasional accessory pituitary (anterior lobe) glands occurring along its course.

b. abnormalities of pharyngeal structures

(1) tongue–Its anomalies consist of:
(a) extremed in size (*macro* and *microglossia*) or complete absence (*aglossia*)
(b) *bifid* or *trifid tongue*–This occurs upon failure of the anlagen to fuse

(2) pharyngeal pouch derivatives
(a) *cysts*, *fistulae* (blind or communicating with the external cleft)–These structures can occur related to any of the pouches. Usually, however, they are related to the second pouch when they exist.
(b) *aberrant* or *accessory thymic tissues*–Such tissue may be found at any point along the course of descent of this organ.
(c) parathyroids–Normally there is considerable variation in the number and in the position of these glands. Intrathoracic parathyroids, for example, are seen.
(d) thyroid–The persistence of a *thyroglossal stalk* or portions thereof (sometimes fistulous or cystic) occasionally occurs. Failure of descent is also seen with the result that the gland is found in the base of the tongue (lingual thyroid).

191

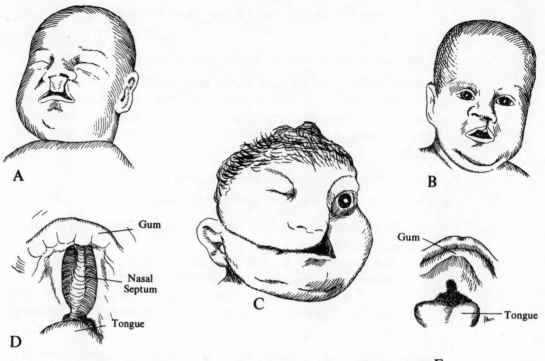

FIGURE **109.** (after Potter, *Pathology of the Fetus and the Newborn*, Yearbook Publishers, Inc.).
A. Bilateral harelip associated with cleft of maxilla and palate.
B. Unilateral harelip without involvement of maxilla or palate.
C. Facial fissure—Unfused naso-optic furrow involving lip, maxilla, and palate.
D. Cleft palate—completed bilateral without involvement of maxilla or lip.
E. Cleft of the soft palate.

   c. abnormalities of the esophagus

      (1) stenosis–This is a narrowing of the esophagus due to hyperplasia of its muscle layer or epithelium, or both.

      (2) *tracheo-esophageal fistula*–This is a communication between these two structures.

   d. abnormalities of the stomach

      (1) transposition–This can be an isolated anomaly or associated with situs inversus.

      (2) incomplete descent–This is usually associated with diaphragmatic abnormalities.

      (3) stenosis–This condition more frequently involves the cardiac or pyloric sphincters.

   e. abnormalities of the intestines

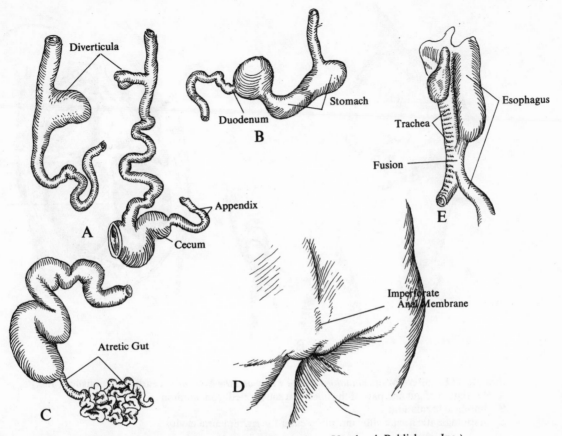

FIGURE **110.** (after Potter, *Pathology of the Fetus and the Newborn*, Yearbook Publishers, Inc.).
A. Meckel's diverticulum—On the left the diverticulum is cone-shaped, on the right its pedicle is smaller.
B. Duodenal atresia with subsequent enlargement of the pyloric segment of the stomach.
C. Jejunal atresia with dilation of the cranial segment of the gut.
D. Imperforate anus (arrow indicating site of anus).
E. Tracheo-esophageal fistula with dilation of the upper part of the trachea.

(1) atresia and stenosis–This is relatively common in the duodenum which normally undergoes a temporary occlusion.

(2) diverticula–These occur especially at site of yolk stalk, e.g. *Meckel's diverticulum* (found in 2 per cent). With retention of the yolk stalk they may form fistulae opening via the umbilicus.

(3) transposition–This may vary from partial to a complete reversal (mirror image) of normal rotation.

(4) herniation–Such herniation of the gut may be either intra- or extra-abdominal.

(5) *rectovaginal fistula*–This is essentially the retention of the primitive cloaca.

193

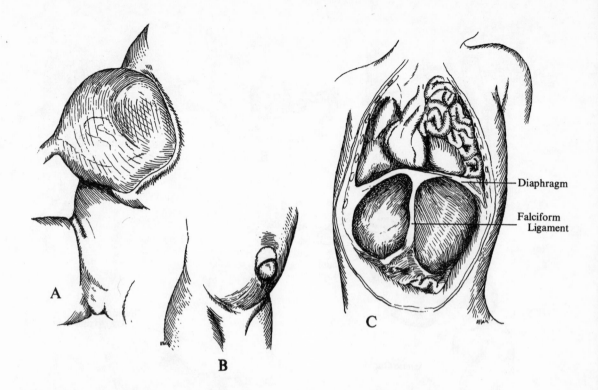

Diaphragm

Falciform
Ligament

FIGURE **111.** (after Potter, *Pathology of the Fetus and the Newborn*, Yearbook Publishers, Inc.)
A. Herniation of gut and part of the liver into sac formed from amnion.
B. Umbilical herniation.
C. Diaphragmatic hernia allowing gut to enter the right pleural cavity.

(6) *imperforate anus*–This is due to the failure of the anal portion of the cloacal membrane to break down.

f. maldevelopment of the accessory organs of digestion

(1) liver and gall bladder
(a) variation of external lobation of the liver
(b) absence or agenesis of the gall bladder
(c) duplication or stenosis of the major bile ducts

(2) pancreas
(a) accessory pancreatic tissue–This is the result of the development of additional primordia or the displacement of the normal primordia.
(b) failure of fusion of dorsal and ventral pancreatic primordia –This results in a doubled pancreas.
(c) variation of ducts–Includes the retention of the *duct of Santorini*, etc.

194

3. Anomalies of the respiratory system (Fig. 110E)

    a. larynx–Anomalies of the larynx are rare and usually consist simply of variation in size.

    b. abnormalities of the trachea

        (1) tracheo-esophageal fistula–This condition is due to incomplete separation of these organs in development.

        (2) stenosis of trachea–This condition is frequently associated with the fistulae noted above.

    c. abnormalities of the lungs

        (1) agenesis–This condition is characterized by absence of one or both lungs.

        (2) variations in lobation–These are common and result in coincident variation of bronchi.

        (3) transposition–As in situs inversus.

4. Anomalies of the urinary system (Fig. 112)

    a. abnormalities of the kidneys

        (1) agenesis

        (2) unilateral rudimentary kidney (usually retaining fetal lobulation)

        (3) *polycystic kidneys*–These result from failure of communication between collecting and secretory tubules. Thus secretions from the latter tubules accumulate within the tubules and form the cysts characterizing this condition.

        (4) positional abnormalities
            (a) pelvic kidney–This occurs due to failure of the kidney to undergo normal ascent.
            (b) horseshoe kidney–The kidneys are fused caudally in this condition.
            (c) unilateral renal mass–This is a relatively amorphous mass of renal tissue.

    b. ureters–These are sometimes doubled due to longitudinal splitting of primordium (metanephric bud or duct).

    c. abnormalities involving the cloaca and bladder

        (1) anal atresia with concomitant rectovesical fistula

        (2) umbilico-urinary fistula (*patent urachus*)

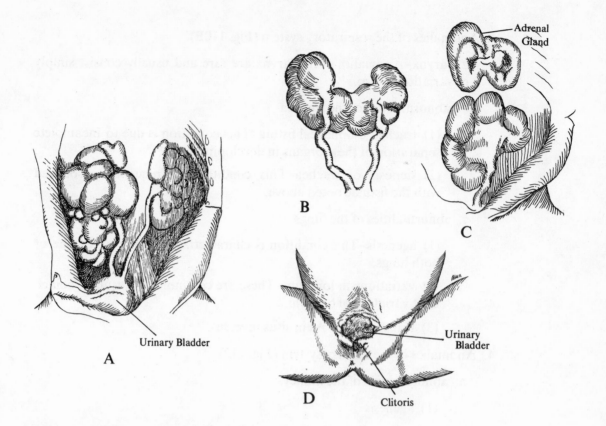

FIGURE **112.** (after Potter, *Pathology of the Fetus and the Newborn*, Yearbook Publishers, Inc.).
A. Polycystic kidney (on the left) compared with a normal kidney (on the right)—note lobulations.
B. Horseshoe kidney.
C. Fused kidneys and fused adrenal glands (above). Note single renal pelvis and ureter.
D. Ectropion of the bladder showing separation of clitoris into paired halves.

      (3) exstrophy of bladder–This is usually due to a ventral body wall defect.

5. Anomalies of the genital system (Figs. 113,114)–These are the result of several factors acting singly or combined, i.e. agenesis, hypoplasia, retention, or exaggeration of primitive structures including those of opposite sex.

    a. *hermaphroditism*–In this condition, the genital organs, or portions thereof, of each sex are found in a single individual.

      (1) true hermaphroditism–In this condition gonads of both sexes are present in the single individual.

      (2) false hermaphroditism–External genitalia of one sex and gonads and internal parts of genital tract of the opposite sex characterize this condition. Many combinations are possible.

196

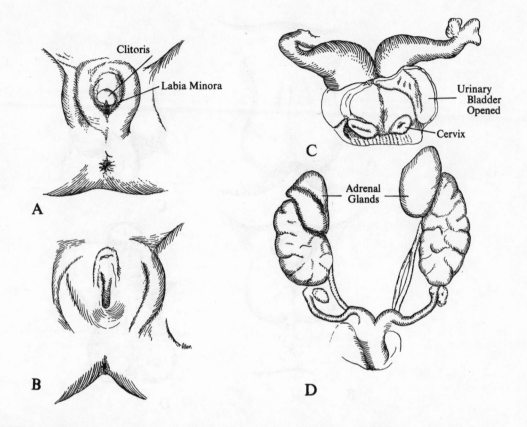

FIGURE 113. (after Potter, *Pathology of the Fetus and the Newborn*, Yearbook Publishers, Inc.).
A. Pseudohermaphroditism—hypertrophy of the clitoris and absence of a vaginal orifice.
B. Agenesis of urethra and vagina—Depression at arrow indicates the position of the vestibule.
C. Complete failure of paramesonephric duct fusion. Note separate cervix on each side.
D. Doubling of the body of the uterus with a single cervix. (Note doubled ureter on the right).

    b. abnormal development in the male

        (1) *cryptorchidism*–This condition results from a failure of testicular descent and is present in 3.4 per cent of full-term deliveries (more frequent in premature births).

        (2) *hypospadias* and *epispadias*–This is characterized by a cleft or even bifid penis. It is due to the failure of fusion of urethral folds.

        (3) agenesis of penis or testis–This condition is rare, although hypoplasia is more common and usually associated with hermaphroditism.

    c. abnormal development in the female–These abnormalities are usually associated with failure of fusion, to a greater or lesser degree, of the paramesonephric (Müllerian) ducts.

197

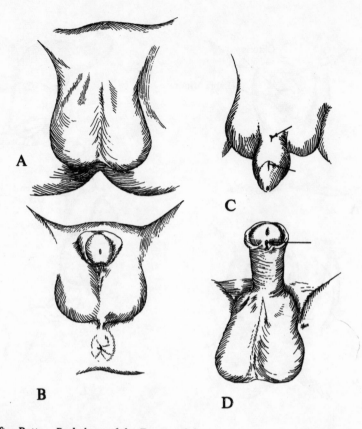

FIGURE **114.** (after Potter, *Pathology of the Fetus and the Newborn*, Yearbook Publishers, Inc.).
A. Penile agenesis—Urethra communicated with the rectum.
B. Penile hypoplasia with hypospadias.
C. Epispadias with urethral openings indicated by arrows.
D. Hypospadias—Urethral opening indicated by an arrow.

(1) uterine anomalies (sometimes including the vagina)
    (a) *bicornuate uterus*-This results in failure of fusion of the primordia (paramesonephric ducts) in the fundus.
    (b) *bipartite uterus*-Partition complete, due to failure of partition between the ducts to break down.
    (c) *bilateral uteri*-Separate uteri result from complete failure of the ducts to unite.

(2) agenesis and hypoplasia-Although this condition is rare, it may include ovaries, all or a portion of the ducts, and the clitoris.

(3) hyperplasia of the clitoris-This condition is sometimes seen and is usually associated with hermaphroditism.

(4) imperforate hymen-Failure of normal break-through at the Müllerian tubercle to occur.

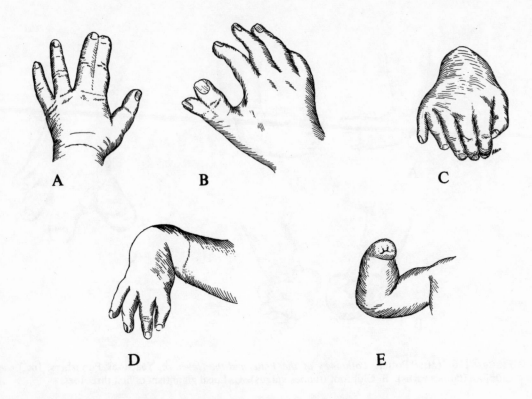

A   B   C

D   E

FIGURE **115.** (after Potter, *Pathology of the Fetus and the Newborn*, Yearbook Publishers, Inc.). A. Syndactylism. B. Duplication of the thumb. C. Polydactylism (bone present in sixth finger). D. Agenesis of thumb associated with absence of the radius. E. Malformation of forearm, hand, and digits.

6. Developmental abnormalities of the skeletal and muscular systems (Figs. 115, 116)

a. skeletal system—Most of these defects follow developmental failure of other structures or systems.

(1) abnormalities of the axial skeleton
(a) *cranioischisis* (*acrania*), *spina bifida*, etc.–These abnormalities are secondarily formed and considered under the central nervous system in more detail.
(b) supernumerary ribs–These are found in cervical and lumbar regions.
(c) cleft or unfused sternal primordia–The cleft sternum is usually associated with ectopic cordis. The less severe condition of a perforated sternum is not uncommon.

(2) abnormalities of the appendicular skeleton
(a) absence of the limbs (*amelia*)–This anomaly obviously involves more than the skeletal elements.

199

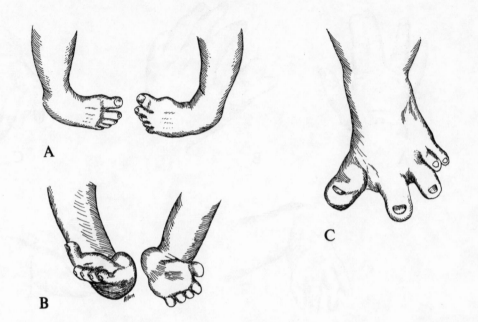

FIGURE **116.** (after Potter, *Pathology of the Fetus and the Newborn*, Yearbook Publishers, Inc.). A. Clubfoot (talipes varus). B. Clubfoot (talipes valgus). C. Local gigantism of first three toes.

(b) absence of clavicles–This is probably due to failure of primordia (intramembranous centers) to appear.

(c) supernumerary digits (*polydactylism*)

(d) fusion of adjacent digits (*syndactylism*)

(e) failure of pubic symphysis closure (usually associated with exstrophy of bladder)

(3) ligaments and joints

(a) failure or incomplete formation of the acetabular fossa— This usually results in congenital dislocation of the hip.

(b) club foot (*talus equinus*)–Many varieties of this abnormality have been described.

b. muscular system–Abnormalities of this system are closely linked with the developmental failure of other structures with which muscles are associated, e.g. incomplete closure of the abdominal wall in umbilical herniation.

(1) muscular absence or weakness–This is relatively common in the abdominal wall and leads to herniation (especially in umbilical region).

(2) anomalous origins and insertions–These variations usually fall within the range of acceptable normality.

200

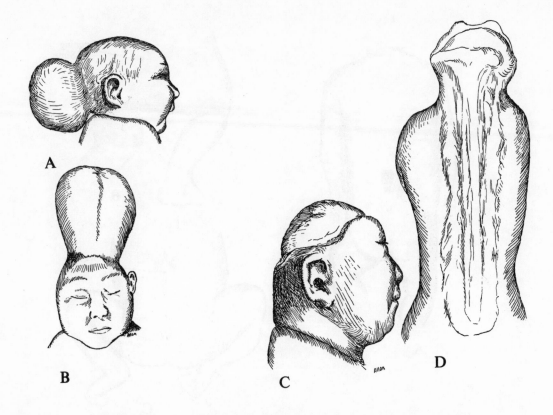

FIGURE **117.** (after Potter, *Pathology of the Fetus and the Newborn*, Yearbook Publishers, Inc.). A. Meningocele. B. Encephalocele. C. Anencephaly. D. Craniospinal rachischisis.

7. Developmental abnormalities of the central nervous system (Figs. 117, 118, 119A)

a. failure of neural tube closure (involves associated mesodermal structures to a variable degree)–This condition gives rise to the following abnormalities which are listed in order of severity:

(1) *anencephaly* or *amyelus*–In these anomalies the brain and spinal cord, respectively, are absent or greatly reduced. Correlated spinal and cranial skeletal abnormalities are, respectively:

    (a) *acrania (cranioschisis)*
    (b) *spina bifida* or *posterior rachischisis*

(2) *myeloschisis*–This abnormality shows an open neural tube (spinal cord) which is also correlated with spina bifida.

(3) *meningo-encephalocoel, meningomyelocoel*, and simple *meningo-coel*–These are conditions in which the brain and its coverings, the cord and its coverings, or the meninges alone herniate through defects in the tissues surrounding the neural tube.

201

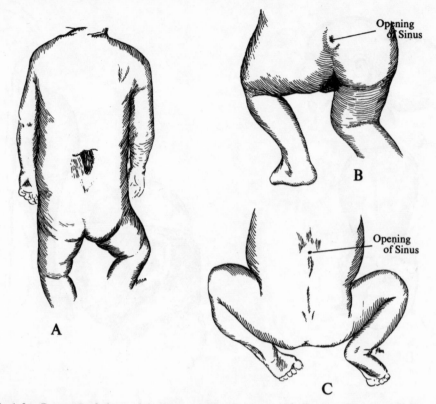

FIGURE **118.** (after Potter, *Pathology of the Fetus and the Newborn*, Yearbook Publishers, Inc.).
A. Spina bifida—Small lumbar defect.
B. Pilonidal sinus—No communication with the spinal canal.
C. Dermal sinus of the lumbar region communicating with the spinal canal (note hairy tufts around orifice).

> (4) *pilonidal cysts*–These develop as remnants of the *filum terminale* of the spinal cord (due, perhaps, to failure of the posterior neuropores to close) and are seen at the tip of the coccyx.

b. maldevelopment of ventricular system–This is usually due to a blocked interventricular foramen or cerebral aqueduct which results in *hydrocephalus* or an accumulation of fluid (cerebrospinal) in the brain.

c. histogenetic maldevelopment–Failure of proper histogenetic differentiation and migration leads to certain types of congenital idiocy.

8. Developmental abnormalities of the peripheral nervous system

a. anomalous relationships–These occur relatively frequently in the various plexuses (brachial and lumbosacral) of the spinal nerves.

b. histogenetic abnormalities

(1) agenesis of sensory nerve endings (*congenital analgia*)

202

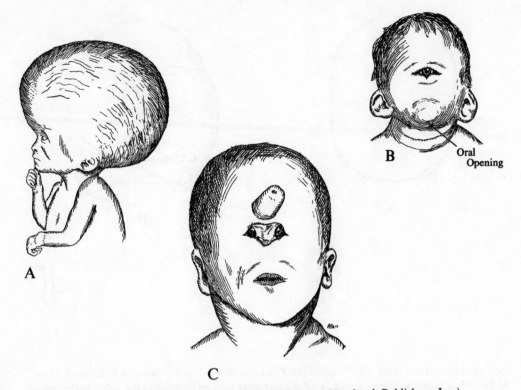

B   Oral
Opening

C

FIGURE 119. (after Potter, *Pathology of the Fetus and the Newborn*, Yearbook Publishers, Inc.).
A. Hydrocephalus due to absence of aqueduct of Sylvius (10 month old infant).
B. Cyclops hyponathus. Nose absent and mouth (beneath protuberance) rudimentary.
C. Cyclops—Central orbit beneath proboscis contains a fuse eyeball with doubled pupil, iris, lens, and retina.

    (2) tumors of peripheral nerves

    (3) tumors of ganglia or chromaffin tissue

9. Developmental abnormalities of the eye (Fig. 119 B, C)

    a. fusion of primordia (*cyclopia*)–This abnormality is characterized by a monster having a single eye (usually located below the nose) in the midline.

    b. *incomplete coloboma*–This condition occurs with failure of closure of the choroidal fissure and is marked by a gap in the iris.

    c. *persistence of pupillary membrane*–This structure lies over, or bridges the pupillary opening.

    d. *congenital cataract*–This condition is characterized by an opaque or cloudy lens. Although the etiology of this condition is not understood, the occurrence of German measles (rubella) in the mother during the first trimester of pregnancy may be an important factor.

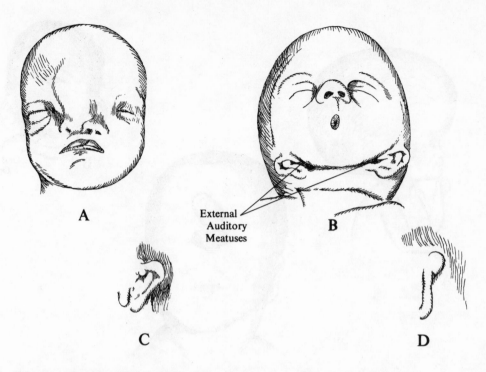

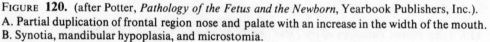

FIGURE **120.** (after Potter, *Pathology of the Fetus and the Newborn*, Yearbook Publishers, Inc.).
A. Partial duplication of frontal region nose and palate with an increase in the width of the mouth.
B. Synotia, mandibular hypoplasia, and microstomia.
C. Satyr ear—Abnormal closure of first external cleft.
D. Hypoplasia of pinna with absence of the external auditory meatus.

10. Anomalies of the ear (Fig. 120B,C,D)

    a. agenesis–Rare.

    b. congenital deafness–This condition may be due to:

        (1) improper nerve connections (*nerve deafness*)

        (2) *atresia* of *tympanum*–This abnormality usually involves imperfect or incomplete development of the tympanic ossicles.

        (3) auricular (pinna) abnormalities–These are most common; due to failure of appearance or fusion of primordia.

        (4) *synotus*–This abnormality is the result of failure of first arch to develop *(agnathia* or *micrognathia)* with fusion of ears ventrally.

11. Anomalies of the integumentary system

    a. abnormalities of the skin

        (1) *ichthyosis*–This condition is characterized by fish or reptile-like epidermal plates.

(2) *naevi*–These are of two types:
    (a) moles
    (b) purplish coloration due to a vascular plexus in the corium

(3) abnormalities of the nails–Evident as misshapen nails or by their absence (*anonychia*).

(4) abnormalities of the hair
    (a) *atrichia*–Absence (*hypotrichia*–deficiency).
    (b) *hypertrichosis*–Excessive hairiness.

(5) abnormalities of the mammary glands
    (a) *amastia*–Absence of one or both mammary glands.
    (b) *polymastia*–Supernumerary mammary glands.
    (c) *polythelia*–Supernumerary nipples. Accessory nipples are present in about one per cent of the population.

b. abnormalities of the teeth

(1) *anodontia*–This is a condition where one or all of the teeth fail to develop.

(2) *polydontia*–In this abnormality supernumerary teeth exist (these can be ectopic or in line with the others, e.g. fourth molars).

(3) *fusion, double crowns*, etc.–These are also observed on occasion.

(4) *cysts*–These are usually developed from tooth buds or incompletely formed teeth which are found within the gum.

GENERAL REFERENCES

AREY, L. B., 1954, Developmental Anatomy. W. B. Saunders, Philadelphia, 6th ed., ix and 680 pp.

DODDS, G. S., 1946, The Essentials of Human Embryology. John Wiley and Sons, Inc., xii and 314 pp.

HAMILTON, W. J., J. D. BOYD, and H. W. MOSSMAN, 1952, Human Embryology. Williams and Wilkins, Baltimore, 2nd ed., viii and 432 pp.

KEITH, A., 1948, Human Embryology and Morphology. Ed. Arnold and Co., London, 6th ed., xii, 690 pp.

KEIBEL, F. and F. P. MALL, 1910–1912, Manual of Human Embryology. J. B. Lippincott Co., Philadelphia, Vol. I, xvii and 548 pp; Vol. II, viii and 1032 pp.

KOLLMAN, J., 1907, Handatlas der Entwicklungs-geschichte des Menschen. Fischer, Jena.

PATTEN, B. M., 1953, Human Embryology. Blakiston Co., Inc., New York, xvii and 798 pp.

POTTER, E. L., 1953, Pathology of the Fetus and the Newborn. Year Book Publishers, Inc., Chicago, xvii and 574 pp.

WINDLE, W. F., 1940, Physiology of the Fetus. W. B. Saunders, Philadelphia, 249 pp.

210

213

Foreskin, *see* Prepuce
Form
    external body, 45–9
Formative cells, 20, 44
Fossa, rhomboid, 149
Fourth ventricle, 150
Fraternal twins, 25
Frontal bone, 131
Frontonasal process, 47
Funiculi, 149

Gall bladder, 96
    maldevelopment of, 194
Gametogenesis, 8–11
    oogenesis, 10–11
    spermatogenesis, 9–10
Ganglia (ganglion)
    cephalic autonomic, 163
    intramural, 163
    pre-aortic, 163
    spinal, 40, 144, 157
    sympathetic, 144, 163
Gartner's
    canal, 124
    duct, 124
Gastrocolic ligament, 106
    gastrolienal ligament, 106
    gastrosplenic ligament, 106
Gene(s), 183
Genetic factors in abnormal de-
    velopment, 183
Genital
    organs
      adult, 5–7
      indifferent stage, 117–20
      definitive stage, 121–5
    ridge, 111, 117
    system, 5–7, 41, 116–29
      accessory organs of, 6,
        128–9
      adult, 5–7
      anomalies, 196–8
      differentiation, 121
      external genitalia, 120
      indifferent stage, 116
      internal genitalia, 116
Germ
    cells, 5, 7, 9–10, 116, 123
    layers, 3, 20
      formation of, 20
German measles, 203

Germinal
    cells, 123 (*see also* Germ,
      cells)
    epithelium, 7, 123
Gigantism, 186
Girdle
    pectoral, 135
    pelvic, 136
Gland(s)
    adrenal, 40, 164
    Bartholin's, 129
    bulbo-urethral, 6, 128
    Cowper's, 6
    lacrimal, 171
    lymph, 79
    mammary, 179
      abnormalities, 205
    parathyroid, 95, 191
    prostate, 6, 128
    sebaceous, 179
    of Skene, 129
    of skin, 179
    sudoriparous, 179
    suprarenal, 40, 164
    sweat, 179
    thymus, 95
    thyroid, 95–6
    uterine, 27–8
    vestibular, 129
Glomerulus,
    internal, 111
    pronephric, 109
Glossopharyngeal nerve, 160
Gonad, 40, 117
Gonadal
    artery, 66
    vein, 71
Graafian follicle, 11–12
Gray matter, 144, 149
Groove(s)
    branchial, 49
    laryngotracheal, 85
    pharyngeal, 174
    urethral, 121, 126–8
Growth
    abnormal, 184, 186
    auxetic, 4
    craniocaudal gradient, 24
    differential, 4
    fetal, 50
    multiplicative, 4

Gubernaculum testis, 123,
    125–6
Gut, 35, 80
    blood supply, 65
    fore-, 85, 93
    hind-, 35, 88
    mid-, 87
    rotation of, 86–8
    tail, 88
Gustatory organs, 166

Hair, 180
    abnormalities, 205
    bulb, 180
    fetal, 181
    follicle, 180
    papilla, 180
Hand, 49
    abnormalities of appendicu-
      lar skeleton, 199–200
Harelip, 191
Harrison, Ross G., 4
Harvey, William, 3
Head fold, 46, 47, 93
Heart, 54–8, 60, 72, 74–5, 77
    abnormalities, 187–9
    atrium, 56, 58–9
    circulation within, 75, 77
    definitive, 58–9
    septation, 56–7
    sinus venosus, 54, 56, 66–8
    valves, 59
    ventricles, 56, 58–9
Hemiazygos, 71
Hemisphere
    cerebellar, 153
    cerebral, 146, 153
    telencephalic, 149
Hepatic
    capsule, 96
    diverticulum, 96
    ligaments, 96
    sinusoids, 96
    swelling, 49
    veins, 66, 68
Hepatoduodenal ligament, 105
Hepatogastric ligament, 105
Hensen's node, 23
Heredity, *see* Gene(s)
Hermaphroditism, 196

215

216

217

enamel, 182
genital, 5–7, 116, 122, 128
gustatory, 166
olfactory, 166
of special senses, 42, 166
spiral, 159, 172
of Zuckerkandl, 165
Organizer, 38
Ossification, 130, 135
endochondral, 130
intramembranous, 130
Otic
pit, 171
placode, 171
vesicle, 47, 49, 171
Otocyst, 171–2
Outflow (autonomic)
craniosacral, 163
parasympathetic, 163
sympathetic, 163
thoracolumbar, 163
Ovary, 7, 10, 12, 122–3
agenesis, 198
cortex, 123
differentiation, 122–3
hypoplasia, 198
positional changes, 123
Ovarian
artery, 66
cycle, 14
Ovulation, 12, 14
Ovum (ova), 3, 7, 10–12, 15–16, 123
development, 11
fate, 15
fertilization of, 11, 15–16
during ovulation, 12
primordial, 123

Palate, 82
cleft, 185, 191
Palatine
bone, 133
muscles, 139
processes, 82, 191
Pancreas, 87
dorsal, 97
ducts, 97
maldevelopment of, 194
ventral, 96
Papilla
dental, 182

dermal, 178
hair, 180
Papillary
ducts, 112
muscles, 59
ridges, 178
Paradidymis, 123
Paraganglia, 165
Paramesonephric ducts, 120, 124–5, 197
Parathyroid gland, 95, 191
thoracic 186, 191
Paraxial mesoderm, 24, 41
Parietal
bones, 131
decidua, 29
Paroophoron, 124
Patella, 136
Pectoral girdle, 135
Peduncles, basic or cerebral, 147
Pelvis, renal, 111
Pelvic
diaphragm, 138
girdle, 136
Penis, 126
abnormal development, 197
glans, 125
prepuce, 126
Pericardial
cavity, 25, 55, 93
swelling, 46, 47, 49
Perilymph, 172
Perilymphatic space, 172–3
Perineurium, 155
Peripheral nervous system, 40, 155–63
Peritoneal cavity, 100, 102
greater sac, 104
lesser sac, 104–6
Permanent teeth, 182
Pharyngeal
arches, 63, 85, 93, 98 (see also Branchial arches)
muscles of, 140
clefts, 85, 174
grooves, 174
hypophysis, 93, 191
pouches, 85, 93, 95, 174
abnormalities, 191
Pharynx, 85, 93
abnormalities, 191
derivatives, 95

Physiology, developmental, 4
Pia mater, 151
Pigment
of hair, 180
layer of retina, 169
of skin, 176
of syncytiotrophoblast, 30, 32
Pilonidal cyst, 202
Pinna, 175
abnormalities, 204
Pit
nasal, 49
olfactory, 47, 82, 166
otic, 171
Pituitary body or gland (see also Hypophysis)
in abnormal development, 186
anterior lobe, 93
posterior lobe, 93
stalk, 93
Placenta, 19, 29–30, 32–4, 52
discoid, 32
fate of, 32
praevia, 33
Placental
barrier, 32
circulation, 31–2, 52
cotyledons, 32
maturation, 32
Placentation, 27, 29–30
Placode
ectodermal, 163
lens, 170
olfactory, 49, 166
otic, 171
Plasma, of blood, 52
Plate (see also Membrane)
alar, 146, 148, 157
basal, 146, 156, 163
chorionic, 32
floor, 146
neural, 38–9, 141
notochordal, 23
roof, 146
Pleural cavity, 100
Pleuro-peritoneal cavity, 25
Plexus, choroid, 150, 154
Polar body, 11
Polydactylism, 200
Polydontia, 205
Polymastia, 205

Sphenomandibular ligament, 133
Spina bifida, 186, 199, 201
Spinal
    canal, 150
    cord
        abnormal development, 201–2
        blood supply of, 65
        central canal of, 149
        columns of, 149
        funiculi, 149
        layers, 149
    nerves, 161, 163
Spiral
    arterioles, 28, 32
    organ, 159, 172
Splanchnic
    arteries, 66
    mesoderm, 20
Splanchnopleure, 24, 36, 40, 81
    of gut, 93
    mesoderm, 24, 40, 52
Spleen, 79
    pulp, 79
    sinuses, 79
Spongiosum, stratum, 17, 28
Stalk
    body, 23, 31, 35, 52
    of hypophysis, 93
    optic, 168–9
    thyroglossal, 191
    yolk, 36, 87, 192
Stapes, 133, 174
Stapedius muscle, 140
Stato-acoustic nerve, 159, 171
Stenosis
    of aorta, 189
    of esophagus, 192
    of intestine, 193
    of stomach, 192
    of trachea, 195
    valvular, 189
Sternocleidomastoideus muscle, 161
Sternum, 134
    bifid, 185
    cleft, 199
    perforated, 199
Stomach, 86, 90
    abnormalities, 192
    curvatures, 90

mesenteries, 89–92
    rotation, 90–92
Stomodeal
    derivatives, 93
    ectoderm, 181
    membrane, 22, 93 (*see also* Membrane, buccopharyngeal, oral)
    structures, abnormalities of, 191
Stomodeum, 46–7, 82, 93, 166
    derivatives, 93
    subdivision, 82
Stratum
    basale
        of endometrium, 17, 28
        of skin, 176
    compactum, of endometrium, 17, 27, 29
    corneum, of skin, 176
    germinativum, of skin, 176
    granulosum, of skin, 176
    lucidum, of skin, 176
    spongiosum, of endometrium, 17, 28
Streeter, George L., 4
Stylohyoid ligament, 133
Stylohyoideus muscle, 140
Styloid process, 133
Stylopharyngeus muscle, 140
Subarachnoid space, 151
Subcardinal
    anastomoses, 71
    veins, 71
Subclavian artery, 64–5
    abnormal development, 189
Subthalamus, 147
Sudoriparous glands, 179
Sulcus
    atrioventricular, 56
    limitans, 145, 149
    optic, 142, 166
Supernumerary
    mammary glands, 205
    nipples, 205
    teeth, 205
Supracardinal veins, 71
Suprarenal (*see also* Adrenal)
    artery, 66
    cortical primordium, 164
    medulla, 164
    vein, 71

Supra-subcardinal anastomosis, 71
Sweat glands, 179
Swelling(s)
    genital, 121, 126
    labial, 127
    lateral lingual, 83
    scrotal, 123, 126
Sympathetic
    chain ganglia, 163
    outflow, 163
    trunks, 161, 163
Sympatho-chromaffin system, 155, 161–5
Syncytiotrophoblast, 18, 30, 32, 44
Syndactyly, 185
Syndactylism, 200
Synotus, 204
System
    alimentary, 41 (*see also* Digestive system)
    cardiovascular, 41, 51–77
    chromaffin, 163–5
    digestive, 80–99
    genital, 5–7, 41, 116–29
    integumentary, 42, 176–8
    lymph, vascular, 78–9
    muscular, 42, 137–40
    nervous
        autonomic, 161–3
        central, 42, 141–54
        peripheral, 40, 155–63
    respiratory, 98–99
    sympathochromaffin, 155, 161–5
    vascular (*see* Cardiovascular system, Lymph, vascular system)
Systemic trunk, 60, 63

Tail, 47
    of spermatozoon, 9–10
Tarsal bones, 136
Taste buds, 166
Tectum, 147
Teeth, 181–2
    abnormalities of, 205
    baby, 182
    bud (tooth), 182
    deciduous, 182
    dentine, 182